A DOCTOR'S ODYSSEY

A Doctor's Odyssey

GEORGE SAVA

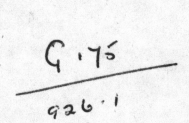

G.75

926.1

FABER & FABER LIMITED

24 Russell Square

London

First published in mcmli
by Faber and Faber Limited
24 Russell Square London W.C.1
Printed in Great Britain by
Purnell and Sons Limited
Paulton (Somerset) and London

CONTENTS

Contents

Part Four

PROLOGUE

To look back on the Italy of twenty years or so ago is like trying to recapture a vivid dream. One is possessed by a sense of urgent, frightening reality, yet one is unable to establish any ordered detail—though some items stand out in impressive isolation, dominating one's thoughts without any apparent logic or intrinsic value. Of course, one could turn to the books—to that vast and remarkable literature inspired by Fascism. But to do so would be to cheat one's memory. What other people saw and experienced was not what one lived through oneself. More than that, most of the books are tendentious, viewing the scene through a particularly coloured pair of spectacles. Moreover, the ordinary man is neither able nor anxious to study current history as a whole; he is aware only of those aspects which affect him personally—and they all too often, particularly of the time and place I have in mind, seem violent, irrational, and, at times, incredible.

So if, in these pages, I write of Florence in 1926, I make no claim to be compiling a history of the times. I was a student in Florence—a medical student; and my chief absorption was with my work, to which the current strife, controversies, troubles, and scuffles were an unwelcome and senseless distraction. Moreover, I had seen enough of revolution and disaster in my own unhappy country to feel none of the native student's urge to take sides and become embroiled in these developments. To an extent no British-born person can understand, participation in politics spelt danger—and specially so to a foreigner. What I set down, then, are only my personal memories, which may be inaccurate (from the historian's viewpoint), confused, or even chaotic, though to me they represent a true picture of those years.

They were times of turmoil and unrest. Mussolini was in power, but not yet established as absolute dictator. He had been feeling his way—for he was always a dictator by accident, an opportunist, rather than a dictator by design and conviction, as Hitler was; and as his sense of security grew stronger, so he became more ruthless and less inclined to tolerate criticism or opposition. By 1926 he found himself able to embark on all those measures of repression and coercion which were to attain their fullest and blackest development at the hands of the Nazis in another country. The merely critical or stiffnecked were given the historical corrective treatment by castor-oil. The open adversaries were banished to rigorous internment in the Lipari Islands, the forerunners of Belsen and perhaps the illegitimate descendants of Sakhalin. The dangerous were murdered. Thus was the cancer cell planted in the body of Western Europe—and it was nobody's business to cut it out before it proliferated to such an extent that a major operation was demanded—an operation that, as we sadly realize, has brought the patient to the very doors of death.

To me and to many students who, like me, were pursuing their studies with difficulty, many of these happenings seemed strange and far away—things that happened and yet had no personal message. In Florence there were demonstrations; people disappeared mysteriously. The dark forces were at work, but not yet prominently in the open. So, at any rate, it seemed to me at the time, though historians may correct me and affirm that Florence was a hotbed of oppression. But these are my personal impressions, as I have said, and no more, and I look back on the scene through my own eyes only. In the medical school there were groups of Fascist and anti-Fascist students, who often waged wordy—and sometimes more than wordy—warfare with each other, but there was nothing remarkable about that, for such partisanship and its vigorous demonstration are part of student-life everywhere.

This tranquillity, whether real or imagined on my part, was suddenly and rudely shattered. Overnight, it seemed, Florence became the centre of all that was fiercest and most ruthless in the whole Fascist doctrine. More than that, it became the birthplace of one of those legends without which irrational movements like Fascism cannot exist.

Of the rights and wrongs—the background facts—of the murder of Giuseppe Menabuoni I cannot speak here, but the broad outline of the affair must be sketched in if my *mise-en-scène* is to be properly presented. His body was recovered from the River Arno, and its discovery aroused instant indignation. The crime itself was of the most brutal kind, as the body witnessed only too obviously; the sentimental background was the sort that would go direct to the hearts of the Italian people, for he was the only son of a widowed mother.

By itself, the Menabuoni murder would have made headline news not only in Florence but also throughout Italy, even though sudden death by violence was never so rare there as in the British Isles and had, since Mussolini's accession to power, become almost commonplace. Circumstances made it a notable event in Fascist history. For in the waistcoat pocket of the dead man was found a membership card of the Fascist Party. Here was a chance that Mussolini and his followers, anxious as they were at that time to sweep aside all traces of opposition, could not miss. The country resounded with their cries. Menabuoni had been murdered for no other reason than that he was a member of the Party. The anti-Fascists had opened their campaign to destroy the Fascists by brutal murders such as this, which would, in due course, lead to armed resistance, so that Italy would again be plunged into chaos. Giuseppe Menabuoni was loudly proclaimed the first Fascist martyr, and the legend the Fascists wove about him was destined to play a part in the development of their movement curiously similar to that of Horst Wessel among the Nazis.

There was in Florence inflammable material enough to make the fires that the Fascists so assiduously fanned. Within a very little while the ancient city, famous for centuries for its art, its culture, and its learning, was, to all intents and purposes, mob-ruled. The Fascists called for reprisals against the dogs who were either direct instigators of the martyrdom of Menabuoni or else condoned it by refusing to give information. The mere fact of not openly accepting the Fascist Party was sufficient to place a man's property and even life in danger; a careless word might be the prelude to a beating. And, of course, there were plenty of people for whom this state of affairs opened a golden opportunity. They fell on the shops and looted them; they held up passengers and took possession of all they had; they beat up and sometimes killed those with whom they were on terms of personal enmity. It is safe to say, without any desire in the world to exculpate the Fascist Party for its role in these developments, that more than one half of the looting and of the crimes of personal violence were carried out by men—and perhaps women—who cared nothing for Fascists or Communists, democracies or dictatorships, Right or Left, but whose only motivation in life was to seize the opportunity of gain and revenge while it was there. The Fascists did not mind; they had hoped for something like this. Did it not show that the whole country was solidly behind them, ready to avenge their martyrs, and crying out for the strong hand that only the Fascists could provide?

Those who want to study the whole facts of the Menabuoni murder will have little difficulty in finding them elsewhere. It is not my purpose to tell their story here. I have given this outline as an introduction to my book for two reasons. The first is that the story gives in a most striking way a picture of the state of Italy at that time—an Italy in which the strongest and most violent passions could be aroused by the most trivial incidents and in which the reason and mental strength of men were already being sapped by slogans and emotional appeals. The second—and more important—reason is that the events had a direct and radical effect on the person with whom this book is concerned. The end of Giuseppe Menabuoni became important to the Fascists—and therefore in the history of Italy; but Menabuoni himself was unimportant in those respects, for if the first martyr had not been there in Florence, Mussolini's men would have found their candidate in someone else and probably in some other place. But to the life of Dr. Giovanni Campo, which I set out to tell in the following pages, the facts that it was Menabuoni and that the matter occurred in Florence were of prime importance.

But for the murder and its aftermath, my friend Giovanni Campo would probably have followed the path of the bulk of his fellow medical students—he would have qualified and worked out his career among his own people. But he became one of those who were involuntarily caught up in the maelstrom of affairs, and the storm threw him so far from his intended course that he never went back to it. For him the murder was a turning point of destiny, one of those occasions when the grim hand of fate seems to take a man by the scruff of the neck and force him into new and sometimes terrifying ways of life. He perforce turned his back on his native land and marched off on a route that eventually took him half-way round the world; and, as violence diverted his original ambitions, so, in the end, it claimed even his life.

Such strokes of fate as this, which tear a young man from the prospect if not of fame and fortune at any rate of modest competence, contentment, and ordered existence, appear often to be part of the burden which Man has to bear for his sins, a part of a blind justice that selects at random and as frequently punishes the innocent as well as the guilty. But when I think of lives such as that of Giovanni Campo, I cannot help wondering whether this is really the truth; I ask myself, in fact, whether it is not mere human blindness that sees in them nothing but tragedy. Indeed, it seems so often that these hard blows of destiny bring out latent talents and capabilities that, without them, would never have been revealed, so that humanity in general would have been the poorer; and humanity in general, Man at large, is surely more important than a single example of the species.

If he had been allowed to follow his intended course, Giovanni Campo would, I am sure, have been a good and successful doctor, relieving suffering and easing the lot of many Italian men, women, and children. But as it turned out, he was forced into situations that demanded something more than the qualifications of a good doctor—places where he needed to display strength of character and fortitude such as the ordinary doctor—fortunately for many of us—never needs to show. More than that, he brought the boons of medicine and healing to places where sickness, deformity, and epidemic were (and are, largely) still looked upon as the work of devils and malign spirits against whom Man is virtually powerless. Fate, in fact, as I see it, chose Giovanni Campo to be a front-line soldier of medicine because he was one of the few who possessed the qualities necessary for that exacting task.

Whether I am right or wrong, these pages will, I hope, enable the reader to judge for himself. Even if they throw no light on the metaphysical problem I have posed, I am bold enough to believe that they will prove interesting in themselves as a record of a man who endured much, suffered much, experienced much, and, in all, was worthy of the title of man and doctor. In them I have set down all that I know of Giovanni Campo, whose friendship I was honoured to enjoy for twenty years and who never ceased to confide in me, even when we were separated by nearly six thousand miles of physical space. For all their inadequacies, they are my small tribute to his memory and his work.

PART ONE

PART ONE

Chapter One

STORM OVER FLORENCE

To the freshman, whether he be in England or America, Germany or Italy, the path of university life is strewn with pitfalls and made hazardous with mantraps. The formal rules and regulations are terrifying enough, but at least they can be ascertained easily by reference to the official publications and notices. It is far otherwise with the unwritten laws and conventions that the students make for themselves or inherit, into which initiation is slow and sometimes painful. In his politics, his dress, his general mode of thought, the university student often tends to the extremes of revolution and defiance of convention, but as regards the life of his own little community he is the most hidebound conservative and traditionalist, and he is eager and emphatic in enforcing his code. So it is that the neophyte has to discover a way of life that seems often at complete variance with the principles observed elsewhere and in an atmosphere that appears overwhelmingly hostile and censorious.

All this is hard enough; but it is doubly hard for the freshman who happens also to be a foreigner with only a smattering of the native tongue, as I was when I went to the medical school at Florence in 1926. For every chance the Italian freshman had of making a mistake, I had two or more; first, ignorance common to all newcomers, and, second, inability to understand the gravity or nature of my offence because of linguistic difficulties. So where the native student might err once and then learn his lesson once for all, I might commit the same sin over and over again for the simple reason that the voluble execrations poured on my head were largely meaningless to me.

Now these things are trivial enough in themselves. Terrible though they appeared at the time, they are laughable now in retrospect and barely worth recalling. Yet it was through one of these affairs that I made the acquaintance of Giovanni Campo—and so began a friendship that was to last a lifetime.

It is an indication of the insignificance of the actual event that, though I have racked my brains, I cannot recall its exact nature. I had transgressed one of the unwritten laws—that is all I can remember—and the whole world seemed for me to have become suddenly full of derisive and cruel enemies whose one delight was to hold me up to ridicule. Because I could not understand, much less offer any sort of reply, I had taken refuge in flight. Alone, I felt that the world was a more friendly place. In the lecture-room and the laboratories I was happy, for there I could hold my own; but among the students I felt hopeless and helpless. Now I found solitude and allowed myself the luxury of selfpity, which surely is one of the least excusable of human frailties.

Suddenly, I heard a step, and my heart sank. Who was this breaking in on my loneliness? When I saw it was a fellow-student—though not one with whose face I was familiar—I grew almost afraid. I did not want any more humiliation, even in private.

But he looked at me gravely and kindly.

'You shouldn't run away,' he said mildly and reprovingly. 'That only makes it worse.'

My mind was so befuddled by my recent experiences that even these simple words in Italian made no very clear impression on my understanding. He sensed my lack of comprehension, smiled slightly, and then, to my delight, repeated the sentences in French. I was overjoyed. I do not claim that my French, then or now, is fluent, but at any rate it was far, far better than my Italian. My heart warmed to him. It was my turn to smile.

Storm Over Florence

He vaulted up on the low stone wall against which I had been leaning disconsolately, and sat there with his legs swinging. Then he began to talk, slowly as though words came with difficulty to him, but with an air of comradeship and friendliness that hitherto I had not found in this place. Mixing French and Italian, he made me see the errors of my ways, gave me advice with a charming hesitancy that had no air of being patronizing, and then began to roam far and wide over many topics.

This was Giovanni Campo. He was young, and I was young; neither of us could lay any real claim to be anything more than boys, though both of us would have been grossly insulted if any third party had not taken our adulthood for granted as self-evident. But even then he showed, as fully developed, those qualities that were to serve him so well throughout his life. It was not his words, which were often hesitant and ill-chosen, but his manner that impressed one with a kindly, warm spirit quick in understanding and ready in sympathy, an intuition of the sufferings and problems of others, and an urgent anxiety to offer help where he thought it was needed and he believed he could provide it. The turn of fortune's wheel changed many things in Giovanni Campo, as it does for most of us. But those qualities of character remained fundamentally the same, maturity only deepening and broadening them and giving them surer, more positive means of expression.

It is difficult to look back across the years and recapture one's first impressions of one who afterwards became a friend. Intimacy gives one the clues to many traits that were not at first revealed, or if they were, were barely noticed at the time. One finds oneself being wise after the event and giving oneself an acuity of judgement of character one never possessed. If one's friend subsequently becomes great or celebrated, one gives oneself a pat on the back for being among the first to recognize innate genius when the rest of the world was blind, though, in fact, one was as unperceptive as the rest. Making all allowances for these amiable weaknesses of humanity, to which I am at least as prone as anyone else, I am certain that, even at that first meeting, when I was grateful for the first words of friendship and kindness I had heard for a long time, I was conscious of the quiet, unobtrusive strength that underlay Giovanni's outwardly retiring mien.

He was not, and never became, the strong, masterful figure of strength that is noticed immediately on entering a crowded room. On the contrary, he might be seen several times among a crowd or group of people and never attract attention. But once his sympathies were touched, the exterior reserve faded, and there stood forth a man rich in determination and courage, and ready, as events were so soon to prove, to defy the world in defence of his convictions.

Yes, it was commonplace enough, that situation in which a distracted freshman received a word of encouragement and sympathy from a student a year his academic senior, but the sequel was not so ordinary. All too often it leads to fresh and bewildering complications for the junior, who finds that the man who was friendly to him in a moment of warmheartedness refuses point-blank to recognize him later. Any such conduct would have been utterly repugnant to Giovanni Campo. At that moment, in all probability, I was no more than a puzzled human creature to whom he felt he could be of service, but he would not confine that service to a single occasion, would not consider it ended by a single act of impulse. He found in me someone with kindred aspirations and outlook, and, above all, someone in whose presence he could abandon the shyness and reserve that kept him at arm's length from many of his contemporaries.

The chance encounter ripened into ever-strengthening friendship, which was, I think and believe, of mutual benefit. Certainly, I gained much from it. Those first few months, which might have been hell on earth to the foreigner-freshman, passed by easily and happily under his unofficial protectorship. He advised me—never with the air of superior knowledge, but in a spirit that suggested he wanted to help me, and so he smoothed my path. My Italian improved rapidly, and the French content in our conversations grew steadily less. I was able to bring an untroubled mind to the pursuit of my studies, which meant a very great deal to me. These are gains for which I was then and must forever be grateful. But I am vain enough to believe, too, that my friendship helped him also, even though in less direct ways than his succoured me. His was a character so full of the waters of generosity and protection that they had to find an outlet if they were not to cause a dangerous dammed-up pressure in his soul. Among the normal run of vigorous, self-confident, even aggressively independent students, he would find few opportunities for such an outlet. By providing them for him, I enabled him to mature as he would have wished to do. But later, though much sooner than either of us dreamed, I was to be able to repay my many debts to him in a more practical form.

They were happy months, those months before the storm broke—so benign to us that we failed to see or, if we saw, take notice of the clouds building up on the fair Italian horizon. We would lie in the shade and talk of many things, but principally of our dreams of the future. He was shrewd for all that he was dismissed by many, professors and students alike, as a bit of a visionary and, above all, what the English schoolboy calls a 'swot'.

Some of those conversations come back to me across the gulf of the years, still tinged with the slightly pathetic eagerness and idealism of youth.

'Wealth?' I remember he said to me once. 'I do not want to be wealthy. The only use of wealth is to use it wisely, and that means for the benefit of others. So a man who sets out to be wealthy, beginning with nothing, becomes so absorbed in the making of money that he doesn't get the opportunity of using it till he is old and his mind has grown stiff and inelastic and probably selfish. Then, instead of employing it for the good of others, he buys himself a castle or builds a villa, and he surrounds himself with sycophantic friends whose only aim is to divert as much of his possessions as they can to their own pockets.'

'You are a cynic, Giovanni,' I said with a smile, though I knew it was not true. 'Besides, not all rich men are like that. There are quite a number who endow hospitals and research centres and charities, aren't there?'

He nodded. 'No, it is not being cynical, but only stating the truth,' he replied. 'And that is where people such as we are come in.'

'I don't think I follow,' I remarked. 'You mean, we become what you called "sycophantic friends"?'

He laughed. It was a pleasant, low laugh. Never, I think, in all my experience of him did I ever hear him indulge in what is known as a 'hearty laugh'; yet when he laughed, one always felt it was through real amusement or sincere good-humour. A man's character is reflected in his laugh, and there was nothing false or meretricious about Giovanni.

'Not quite. It's a role I don't fancy myself in at all,' he said. 'No. I mean it's up to people like us who believe that men have a duty to their fellow-men more important than their duty to themselves to encourage the rich to divert their money into the right channels and see that it's spent properly. It's really as simple as that,' he went on with boyish eagerness, his eyes alight. 'They make the money, and we spend it for them. That's how the world ought to be organized.'

'It sounds a good idea. What would you do with the money?' As he answered my question, his gaze was set on the far horizons of a vision.

'I'd organize, first of all, a fleet of travelling clinics— you know, lorries equipped as medical stations like they had in the war, only much, much better, and I'd send them up and down the length and breadth of Italy so that everyone, even in the smallest village, could have the best medical attention. And then I'd set up a central organization where there'd be really ample funds and facilities for research—yes, ordinary research on disease up to a point, but principally directed to finding out the right way of living so that people need never get ill. That's the doctor's real job, you know,' he added thoughtfully. 'He ought to stop people from getting ill and not simply try to cure them afterwards.'

It was the young, ardent, perhaps impractical student talking; yet also it was the essential spark within him, the spark that fed the fires of his life to the end.

'You know, George,' he went on soberly, 'I come from a poor village, but it's a better one than many. At least we've got some cobblestones in the street and there are deep wells so that we don't have to drink water that comes out of the river into which all the people throw their garbage and their slops. Yet for all that it would make you feel sick. It's a breeding place of all manner of disease, one of those places from which epidemics start. The people born there have practically no chance at all. The old huts are rotten with lice and bugs. There are rats everywhere —and you know what all that means. That's why my great ambition is to take medical service outside the cities to the people who want it. Oh, and another thing— I almost forgot, and it's so important. I'd endow a whole lot of scholarships for people from villages like my own to become doctors, because it's only people who've been born and brought up in those conditions who know what the real conditions and problems are. It's easy for the townsmen,' he added scornfully. 'They say: "Oh, they need drains and a proper water supply, and they must be taught to wash themselves and practise decent standards of living." Yes, all that, George—all that. But how—how? That's the question the town-bred doctor and research worker can't understand.'

'It's a wonderful idea, Giovanni,' I observed, 'but your rich man would have to be very, very wealthy to endow all that. It'd need a good many millionaires, you know. I think you've mistaken your vocation. You ought to be a politician and get the proper laws passed and State funds turned to this work. I'm not a socialist by any means, but it sounds too big a job for private endowment to tackle all on its own.'

'Politics!' he snapped. This was the first time I had ever seen him utterly and venomously contemptuous. 'The politician is the selfish man—the complete egotist—*par excellence*. I know some of them want to see reforms and improvements, but why—why? Simply because they believe that they themselves will be retained in power, which is what they enjoy above all else. Politicians' reforms, George, are based on the principle of bribes. They say, in effect, "We'll give you this, that, and the other" —it doesn't matter what it is, anything from the moon to a set of drains—and then they add: "But you must see to it that we stay in power."

'Besides,' he continued, 'this isn't politics. What I talked about hasn't anything to do with political creeds. It's just applied medical and sanitary science. It all depends on scientific facts, not on any politician's latest theory. These things are outside and above politics.'

'They ought to be,' I returned, 'but they aren't.'

'No. If only people would come to see that they ought to be governed by the same sort of scientific thought and the same sort of scientific processes as they have their motor-cars manufactured or their houses built! You couldn't sell a car built on nothing more than someone's belief, but you can run a country on it.'

He had never been quite as expansive as this. I was young, too, ambitious, and strong in my insistence on the paramountcy of scientific logic, but, even so, I could not help feeling that, like the politicians he despised so much, he, too, was reaching for the moon.

There was little chance that, in the hectic condition of Italy at the time, either of us could retire to an ivory tower of scientific idealism and ignore the importance of politics; and a day or two after that well-remembered conversation the very foundations of Florence were shaken by the violence of political upheaval. It was then, as I have told in the Prologue, that the Menabuoni murder occurred.

When men's most turbulent passions are released, no one, be he professor or postman, student or sweeper, can stand aside unmoved. There is no malady of the human kind more contagious and infectious than hate and suspicion. In the twinkling of an eye, every student had tied a metaphorical label on himself: he was either Fascist or anti-Fascist. He either believed that Menabuoni was a new St. Stephen, the first martyr of the New Faith, or else he regarded the whole affair as a frame-up conceived on the most mendacious and outrageous lines.

And Giovanni Campo did his best to remain true to his principles and stand outside the controversies, which were rapidly deteriorating into riots.

I recall how once one of the more dictatorial of the avowed Fascist students seized upon Giovanni and tried to find out exactly where he stood. What did he think of this foul murder? Wasn't it right that Menabuoni was a martyr and all who even so much as silently approved of the murder ought to be severely punished? And this brigand left Giovanni in no doubt of possible evil consequences for himself if he so much as hesitated in approving the Fascist theses.

But Giovanni, with that quiet, unaggressive determination of his, would not be shifted from his own point of view.

'How can I express an opinion of any value?' he asked. 'I know nothing of the facts, and this is a question that can be decided only by ascertaining the facts. All we know is that Menabuoni was murdered and his body thrown in the Arno. Who did it, we don't know. Why it was done, we don't know.'

'I see,' sneered the brigand. 'Then you're one of these anti-Fascists. You're morally guilty yourself of the outrage.'

Giovanni stared at him in genuine astonishment. He was completely at a loss to understand how a man already in the fourth year of a medical course, as the brigand was, could be so utterly illogical.

'I'm neither Fascist nor anti-Fascist,' he replied stoutly. 'All I say is that until all the facts are known and independently established it's impossible to hold any opinion worth while.'

'Oh! So that's it,' snarled the other. 'I say he was murdered as part of a terror-plot to exterminate all Fascists. Do you say I'm a liar?' He glowered threateningly.

But still Giovanni remained calm.

'I can only call a man a liar,' he answered rather pedantically, 'I can only call a man a liar when the facts are known and he makes an assertion contrary to those facts. Here, the facts aren't known.'

For one horrible moment I thought the brigand, who was several times more powerful than my friend, was going to strike Giovanni; but he held his peace, such as it was.

'All right,' he snapped. 'I see. The time's coming when you'll find it isn't healthy to sit on the fence, Campo. You'll have to be a man then and make up your mind.'

With that he went away, leaving us both rather shaken. I had kept my mouth firmly shut. I was a foreigner, and, as such, had no right to interfere in matters of domestic politics like this.

It was useless, however, for Giovanni to appeal to scientific method. Already the rude argument of force was replacing the cold logic of reason. Barely a day passed without some scuffle between bands of students of Fascist and anti-Fascist views. Work and study were forgotten, and pitched battles were waged in an environment dedicated to the pursuit of learning and the arts of healing. An incautious, but wholly innocent, remark by a lecturer was sufficient to act as a spark on the tinder of the students' minds, and the theatre would be transformed into a scene of bloody combat. Nor was it an affray merely of fists. Italian blood is hot and tempestuous, and the

Italian himself a natural user of arms. Chairs were used as personal weapons and as missiles, and authority, deeming discretion the better part of valour, did little or nothing to enforce order, fearing, no doubt, that with passions so high any attempt at discipline would make it a common enemy and draw on its head a combined attack. Nor were chairs the only armaments. Anything served. Bottles of specimens flew through the air, exploding like shells to discharge their often grisly contents amid showers of spirit. Indeed, neither sense nor caution was displayed on either side. A jar of acid was as good a weapon as—or even better than—a bottle containing a frog in spirit, and the chemical laboratories became deserted places into which no-one with any desire for personal security ventured.

The riots mounted in a steady crescendo. The latest was always more violent than the one that had preceded it, and advantage, so far, lay with neither side. Daily the situation worsened, and it was clear that sooner or later authority would have to act with a firm hand. Giovanni stood aloof, eyeing it all with distaste.

'How horrible all this is, George!' he exclaimed. 'Suppose one side or the other overcomes its adversary, what does it prove? Nothing—except that the victorious party is either more numerous or more vigorous. Besides, I doubt if the majority know why they're fighting. They howl witch-words at each other, and that's sufficient to turn them into beasts.'

His determination not to take part in these early struggles earned for him a reputation for cowardice and weakmindedness, which made him equally detested by either faction. More than ever, I stood in a special relation to him, his only friend and confidant, and some of the obloquy directed towards him flowed over on me. For my part I asserted and reasserted firmly that I was a foreigner with no right or intention to take sides.

And at last authority acted, but hardly in the way that Giovanni or any logical person might have expected. It happened as the climax of the most macabre and fiercest battle that had yet been fought. The setting was nightmarish. For this occurred in a dissecting-room. Tempers mounted higher and higher, until finally all control was lost. This was the danger point. The search for bigger and better missiles was never more zealous. But luckily it was not dissecting instruments that took the rioters' fancy; perhaps they seemed small and inadequate though they would have been capable of inflicting deadly wounds. Instead, the combatants seized portions of the dead bodies on which they were supposed to be working in the cause of truth and science. In a moment, the air became thick with the dismembered portions of the human frame. Arms, legs, ribs, even skulls, hurtled in all directions.

This was truly serious. A thigh bone, wielded by a young, lusty, and inflamed student, can be a damaging weapon, and other bony parts were hardly less so. Groans, trails of blood, and felled young men, heedlessly trampled underfoot as they lay, gave witness to the fact.

Here was something to which even the eye of university discipline could not be blind; yet equally university discipline was powerless to assert itself. It had wavered too long, and whatever respect it had ever held was long since lost. The police were called, and it was not long before some sort of order was restored. A score or more students were bundled off under arrest.

The efficiency of the police had been remarkable. They had made their arrests with unerring precision, as though guided by some highly developed instinct to their prey. Nor were the selected culprits always those who had been the most violent, either in battle among themselves or in resisting the police.

Yet there was no mystery. The police method of selection was only too plain when the check was made. Without exception their victims had been of the anti-Fascist group. Not a single Fascist was among the arrests. It was a sign of the times, of the iron hand that was closing on the land. Objective truth no longer mattered. The police were no more the nominal servants of even-handed and impartial justice, but agents of the Fascist Party. And it was there, in a university founded for the discovery of knowledge and the exaltation of fact, that they revealed the new design of life.

Chapter Two

THE NEW CHAMPION

Not even the most aloof scientific detachment could remain untouched by the passionate sea of politics which swept not only over Florence but over the university itself. No other thought appeared to have any importance to men, for the most casual comment was likely to provoke a partisan diatribe—which, in the end, meant almost certain trouble. One could no longer be frank with friends or seeming friends; first one had to discover their political alignment. It was a time in which sail-trimming was a much more valuable talent than honesty. Nor was it of much avail to seek refuge in a prudent silence; one had to make open declaration of allegiance—or so the Fascist groups, now in the ascendant everywhere, tried to insist. Of course, those who wanted nothing more than a peaceful life to pursue their studies gave lip-service to the dominant Party. The same thing was happening in the larger world outside the walls of the university. It is through this indifference, this disinclination of ordinary folk to become involved in hot faction, that dictators of all colours rise to power.

But though authority had shown its hand as being composed of Fascist cards which were to be trumps on all occasions, there was still plenty of anti-Fascist activity even after the affair in the dissecting room. Hot-headed students were not going to change their beliefs simply because some of their number had been removed to the doubtful comfort of a Florentine prison-cell. On the contrary, these unlucky ones immediately became martyrs and heroes, victims of a gross and damnable injustice. For a little while, in fact, the anti-Fascist strength increased, augmented by waverers whose indignation was aroused by the police action. There was nothing of potential counter-revolution in this, for waverers are a poor acquisition to any cause; the next turn of Fortune's wheel may send them stampeding to the opposite camp.

Giovanni Campo was not a waverer, but, equally, he was not a partisan. The mere idea of taking sides and resorting to violence in defence of a mere political belief was revolting to his whole character. With might and main, he strove to stand aloof from it all. Yet it was obvious that he could not long maintain this attitude of splendid isolation. His innate strength was too great for that, and in due course injustice must make its mark on him.

'Emotion—hysteria!' he exclaimed to me, as we watched, some distance away, one of the now incessant brushes between hostile groups. 'There is only one possible good outcome of this sort of thing—and that is that all these fools should wipe each other out. They're unworthy to bear the name of Man. Don't they know it's reason that has made man—the power of thinking and judging—and that without reason they're just brute beasts?'

'You're getting sentimental and idealistic, Giovanni,' I retorted. 'I know that fundamentally it's true about reason, but how many people possess the power of choosing scientifically between two alternatives? You're dreaming of an impossible world in which everyone is a philosopher.'

'So you think we should take sides,' he said reflectively. 'All right, then—which side should we be on?'

I smiled at him. 'What is this, Giovanni?' I asked mockingly. 'Are you trying to set a trap for me and get me to declare myself—me, a foreigner here on sufferance?'

For a moment he almost believed I was serious, then he laughed—but it was a bitter, sardonic laugh.

'You're right, George,' he commented. 'It's dangerous even to open one's mouth these days, and one even has to be careful in choosing the colour of one's shirt—though on aesthetic grounds I'm not likely to wear a black one. It's all so stupid. All I ask is to exercise the right of a man to speak the truth as he sees it.'

That was the trouble. For whatever reason, too many people had begun to believe or persuaded themselves that truth was to be found only in one particular set of beliefs or rules, at any rate so far as politics were concerned. From that it followed that all who denied those truths were bearers of false witness with no right to free expression. The philosophical clash was even then growing dangerous; today, it has split the world into two camps.

Day by day the strength and arrogance of the Fascists grew. Organized resistance to them had almost broken down, and the bullies' chief sport now was to seize some inoffensive individual and apply what they called 'appropriate measures' to induce him to abandon his indifference or his neutrality. A sound beating was the least painful of these measures.

Yet though we were conscious of a growing tyranny, few of us outside the fanatical sections of the Fascist groups anticipated that the situation could develop any further. We would be allowed on sufferance provided we held our peace and did not mind an occasional unpleasant half-hour when the masters thought they would like a little enjoyment in their own style. There would be bullying on a major and minor scale. Those things were part of the mad order that was coming into the world. For all that, the thought that there would be any active interference with the normal curriculum of the university never entered our heads. A university was a place for study, where young men prepared to be lecturers and philosophers, historians and doctors, linguists and scientists; it was not an arena of party warfare.

How green we were in those days when the technique of totalitarianism was still being forged, at any rate so far as Western Europe was concerned! And the odd thing is that though I had been brought up in Russia—Imperial

Russia—a land of censorship and suppression and official interference in every phase of life, the idea that anything of that kind could occur in Western Europe never occurred to me as worthy of discussion.

The Voice of Rome spoke. It did so with an authority never possessed by the Popes, once rulers of Rome, in their heyday. Its words were sharp and unambiguous. There was too much disorder in the universities. Young men and women were being encouraged to entertain ideas that were dangerous to the State. It was vital that all centres of learning should equip these young people to play their proper part in the great Corporate State that the genius of *Il Duce* was creating. Henceforth, therefore, all students must belong to the University Fascist Party, of which there would be branches, properly organized, in each university. . . .

These ordinances spread like wild fire throughout the students, who gathered in excited mobs at every convenient point. The Fascists were, of course, elated, and did nothing to disguise their triumph. If possible, they became more arrogant than ever as representatives of a chosen caste. 'You see?' their whole manner suggested. 'It is quite useless to oppose us—we are your masters.'

Giovanni, studying these new commands, look troubled. Then he glanced at me.

'There's a very curious omission,' he said, tapping the official paper. 'They say all students *must* join the University Fascist Party, but they don't say what will happen to those who refuse.'

It seemed a quite insignificant point to me. The Fascists were bosses and we had already seen what happened to those who disagreed with them even before this last mark of official support.

'Does it matter?' I ask. 'Everyone will join to save their skins. You don't propose to refuse, do you?'

'Are you suggesting I should be such a moral coward as to make myself safe by obeying this order?' he demanded quietly but with a look of iron resolution. 'I shouldn't have thought it possible of you, George. Even if I supported the Fascists as a Government and approved of their general principles, I should still fight against an order like this. It's a direct attack on the whole foundation of learning and science. You can't put knowledge into political leading strings.'

This was the first time I had heard Giovanni show signs of wanting to take sides. Trouble loomed ahead, for already I knew of his unfailing determination and courage once his mind was made up firmly.

' "I abhor your views, but I would fight to the death for your right to express them",' I quoted—or misquoted. It was the only comment I could think of at the moment.

He nodded. 'That is the whole principle of freedom of thought in a sentence,' he agreed, 'though I forget who said it. But first we must find out the true position.'

That night there was to be a meeting of all the students, when the new order would be explained to them. The large hall was packed, and I do not think a single student was voluntarily absent. Giovanni was one of the first to arrive; he had insisted on the need for being early as he wanted a position near the speaker's rostrum. Rather unwillingly I sat beside him in the very front row; if any trouble started, that was likely to be one of the warmest of spots, and it was a prospect I did not relish.

The proceedings began quietly enough. It was all quite simple, the speaker, who was President of the University Fascist Party, explained. All it meant was that students had to make an open declaration that they would not oppose the Government and the steps it was taking to restore Italy to her rightful place among the greatest nations of the world. He added that there had been a good deal of demonstration lately, which showed the existence of riotous and subversive elements. It was those authority wanted to keep in check, and the ordinary student would not be affected. If all joined the Fascist Party and subscribed to its principles, trouble must cease, because the Party itself could keep its members under proper control.

As it went, it was a mild speech, bearing in mind the point of view it had to represent. But then the Fascists were still not absolutely sure of themselves. Open opposition to them still existed, and in considerable strength at that. The position of single party dictatorship under the absolute direction of a single Leader had not yet been reached. It was not far in the distance, and these orders were part of the plan to establish it, yet a need for caution still existed.

No sooner had the speaker finished, than Giovanni sprang to his feet.

'Can you say what would happen to any students who refused to join the Party?' he demanded bluntly.

One could feel the tension in the hall suddenly increase. A murmur ran round the students. Giovanni Campo, the intellectual isolationist, was the last person they had expected to put a question of that kind—and so directly.

The President smiled disdainfully. 'I do not think there will be many who would refuse to conform with so sensible a direction,' he observed, with a faint hint of threat, nevertheless, in his voice. 'But there are fools everywhere, even in a university—and not only fools but rash fools. I can only say that those who refuse would do so at their own peril.'

'Of what?' demanded Giovanni in a clear, challenging voice.

'That would be for authority to decide,' was the reply. 'The numbers are likely to be so small, I think'—again there was that suggestion of menace—'and there would be no rigorous punishment of the kind that might exalt them to the status of martyrs in some people's eyes. I will only say that they might find life a little inconvenient and'— he paused significantly—'perhaps unpleasant.'

'In what ways?' persisted Giovanni, determined to tie the man down to a more precise statement. 'Expulsion?'

'Expulsion is something for the University to consider. I am merely the representative of the University Fascist Party and not of the governing body. From my point of view I can only say that, naturally, those who failed to join the Party would not enjoy any of the advantages of Party membership. Simple, isn't it? They would not, for example, be able to use the libraries or the students' restaurants, which, from now on, will be controlled by the Party. I mention those as examples—there might be others.' He smiled.

A fresh murmur ran round the hall. The penalties looked simple enough, but they were serious. Denial of access to the libraries meant that non-Fascist students would have almost insuperable difficulties in their studies. Exclusion from the restaurants would be a heavy blow, since that would mean no more cheap and good meals. Few of the students were rich in those days in Italy; the cost of living in cafés in the city would be prohibitive to almost all.

The President waited for the murmur to die down, then he raised his hand for silence.

'But why talk about such unpleasant things as this?' he asked suavely. 'I am sure none of us here would be so ill advised.'

Then occurred one of the events that is most vividly impressed on my mind of my period at Florence. Amid a deep and expectant silence, Giovanni walked slowly up the short flight of steps leading to the platform, while the President stared at him in blank astonishment.

Giovanni faced him.

'Here is one, Mr. President,' he said in a clear voice that reached everyone in that packed audience. 'I shall not join the Party. That does not mean that I am politically anti-Fascist or Fascist. I am no meddler in politics, but a student with ambitions to be a doctor. A university is a place of learning whose full facilities should be available to all admitted as students. None should be denied solely and simply because he does not wear a particular political label. That is against all the principles of justice, freedom, and the tradition of culture. It is monstrous. If a student is undesirable, then the governing body can deal with him.

If he threatens the State by his political activities, the police can take notice of it. I am here, Mr. President, to protest in the name of truth and liberty and . . . '

The Fascist majority could endure no more, while the President went purple in the face at this amazing affront and defiance. Perhaps the only calm person in the whole hall was Giovanni Campo, standing there on the platform, his face coldly determined, but a little pale, while a tremendous storm broke round him. Ushers stepped forward and began to handle him roughly. In the body of the hall, scuffles were already breaking out. Pandemonium threatened.

What might have happened to Giovanni at the hands of the ushers and marshals I do not know; they were anxious to do their worst to this brazen defier of Fascist authority to rule men's minds as well as their public actions. But Giovanni's bold speech had had a remarkable effect. Open anti-Fascist feeling had been growing noticeably less since the police intervention, and the latest ordinance had appeared to crush it completely. The defiance fanned the dying embers into leaping flame. A mass of students—it might have been fifty or even a hundred—forced their way to the front and tore Giovanni, who had been making a stern and heroic fight against odds, from the grasp of the Fascists. This done, they formed a phalanx round him, hitting out with their fists and feet—it was no time for niceties—and with any convenient weapon that came to hand. Already there were plenty of broken chairs, and their legs made admirable bludgeons. So they battled their way towards an exit door, their courage and determination more than counterbalancing their numerical inferiority to the Fascists. Surrounded by a riotous mob, I was unable to move. The last I saw of Giovanni and his bodyguard was a seething, fighting mass jammed in the doorway.

From that moment in the hall, Giovanni became a transformed man. Hitherto he had been reserved, quiet, almost unnoticed by the bulk of the students, even those of his own year pursuing the same courses. Now he found himself suddenly erupted to the position of anti-Fascist leader, a popular champion of liberty round whom all opponents of Fascism could rally. This was astonishing enough; but it did not astound me so much as his acceptance of the position.

'I can't understand it,' I said to him. 'You've always held so aloof from politics and movements—and now you're working night and day running what amounts to a minor counter-revolution.'

'That isn't quite true, George,' he answered soberly. 'This goes deeper than politics. I belong to no political group or system. I'm not a Fascist or a Liberal or a Socialist or a Communist or a Republican or anything else. I don't mind much what the system of government is provided it guarantees freedom of thought and freedom of expression and freedom for the ordinary man to go about his innocent affairs without being forced to believe this or that as inspired truth. That's something that cuts right across all this folly of parties. But once a government starts dictating what a man shall believe and starts distinguishing between people, saying that some may learn and others mayn't, it ceases to be government and becomes tyranny. It's going back to the Dark Ages. You know how I hate faction and violence, George, but there are times when everyone has to make a choice whether he will fight for a basic principle of right or meekly submit to dictation. I have made my choice, and nothing will move me from it.'

Like all Giovanni's statements, it was all very quiet, very controlled, and very determined; and for that reason it was all the more convincing and terrible in its force. Here was no hothead who had imbibed slogans and theories. No; here was a man who hated insincerity, hated enslavement, hated all that, as the years were to show, Fascism stood for, though it had not then been revealed in full. The voice that had spoken was the voice of intense and fearless moral courage. From that moment, I respected

The New Champion

Giovanni as I have respected few men; for in few men have I found the same qualities—which is not surprising, for they are among the rarest of the great human virtues. I use the word 'great' deliberately, for in Giovanni were the makings of greatness—that greatness which need not show itself in high position, but always reveals itself in singleminded service whether it be to a cause, an ideal, or the practice of the humanities.

Giovanni saw clearly, with his fine logical brain, the dangers into which he was marching; but danger was the last thing to deter him. I do not think fear existed for him when his mind was made up to a certain course of action, for the simple reason that he never arrived at a conclusion without having focused on it quite exceptional powers of mental analysis. He was to show those powers throughout his chequered life.

Just because he was so restrained and thoughtful, just because he detested violence, he rallied the waning anti-Fascist students to a new and purposeful unity. He appealed not to emotion, but to reason. And he was intensely practical. For example, to overcome the ban on the use of the libraries, he arranged a pool of books for his own followers, and he even contemplated running a café service to replace the students' restaurants.

I think he knew he was fighting a vain battle, and that, in the end, the weight of force and numbers on the other side must overcome him. He saw, too, that finally he must find himself opposed not to a domineering, hostile group within the university but to the State itself, whose authority he was, in effect, challenging. For the orders for students to become Fascists was not a university decree but an edict from Rome itself. Arrest, denunciation as an agitator or traitor, transportation to the ill-famed Lipari Islands—these were clearly before his eyes, but they did not raise so terrible a prospect as the secret murder beneath the sticks and boots of the hooligans who called themselves the saviours of the country and the apostles of pure truth.

The New Champion

Not a day passed without his receiving a warning of some kind or other; that of murder—or 'rightful death', as one anonymous screed had it—was not infrequent. Yet so far he was not openly challenged by the Fascists. His moral courage and calmness overawed them—at any rate for the time being. He was rarely molested, and even when he was the effects were trivial.

Yet, as I have said, he could see what the end would be. He would never acknowledge defeat while he had breath, but might would prevail.

Serene as ever, he looked at me on an occasion I vividly recall, and smiled a little sadly.

'It's a queer world, George. You, in your Russian way, would talk of destiny, but I prefer to say it's all chance. I set out to be a doctor and now I find I'm a political agitator, a marked man whose life isn't worth a flip of the finger. From the puzzles of life and the living, I've been switched to contemplation of certain death sooner or later by violence. Yet someone had to do it,' he added in a low voice as though he was reassuring himself.

'Yes,' I remarked, taking up the last sentence. 'Someone has to do these things. It would be a poor world without people like you, Giovanni.'

'There's no credit to me,' he protested. 'If it hadn't been I, it would have been someone else.'

He may have been right, for the Giovanni Campos of this world are rare and precious personalities. All I know is that, by chance, I had spoken words that very, very many people were afterwards to echo as an undeniable truth. It would, indeed, have been a poorer world without Giovanni Campo.

Chapter Three

THE LAST THROW

So much happened in those troublous days that memory for detail necessarily grows fogged and obscure. It tends, rather, to present a general and overshadowing impression of one nightmarish horror—the mounting persecution and oppression, and the personal wounds that faction inflicts, for erstwhile friend becomes antagonized from friend and the criterion of companionship ceases to be individuality and becomes acceptance or denial of a political creed instead. Yet above all this one clear, sharp picture rises—that of Giovanni Campo, serene, courageous, single-minded, in some subtle way detached from the general turmoil yet essentially part of it, like a soaring seabird over a tumultuous ocean.

If I am asked to give a picture of Giovanni, it is the figure of those days that first comes to my mind. Worry and anxiety had drained most of the colour from his naturally olivine face, above which the black hair swept back in a smoothly brushed curve, which always reminded me of the scroll at the head of a violin. His dark eyes had that unblinking alertness which comes to men who see a vision clearly and who are aware, too, of dangers threatening on every hand; one felt that not the slightest detail escaped that searching gaze. His long, artistic hands, always eloquent of gesture, were now used forcefully in a way that he never had shown before and was not to reveal later. His every movement had an air of determination—not the strutting swagger of the Fascist bully who knew that he had force on his side, but the quiet directness and purposiveness of the man whose mind is made up unequivocally.

In some ways, I think, this was one of the most important periods of self-realization in all Giovanni's variegated life. It is a mere truism to point out that his experiences then converted the diffident student into the mature and self-reliant, self-knowing man. What I feel about this phase is that it was a rebirth for his spirit. He broke out of the narrow confines of outlook that would have bound him to the round of the doctor and teacher, and learnt that, before one can be either, one must be first a man in the highest sense. He realized also that self-affirmation is the greatest thing in the development of character; and by that I do not mean aggressiveness, but the power to embrace a principle or an ambition and hold to it whatever may befall. He was converted from the passive looker-on, ready to lift a critical shoulder at the emotional and, as it appeared to him, ridiculous broil of politics, to one who understood that action no less than thought must play its part in the well-balanced man who would serve humanity. And also he became ready to be a leader, even though leadership was thrust upon him.

Of course, all these changes were not sudden. The student did not metamorphose into the anti-Fascist leader in the full sense overnight or in the twinkling of an eye. It was a slow growth, and some of its fruits did not come to ripeness till long after; that fact, in itself, testifies to the deep and searching experience he underwent; and naturally his first tendency was to swing from one extreme to the other. The quiet, methodical, yet brilliant, student, for whom the university had hitherto existed as a place where he could gather knowledge, suddenly seemed to lose primary interest in his work. He saw the university now as a microcosm of the outside world, a place in which the struggle must be fought out once and for all between dictatorship and freedom; and he felt that, just because a university was a cradle of culture, so its solution of the problem should be an example to all those in the country who through lack of education and opportunity were incapable of judging the issue by fact alone and were accordingly to be swept along by uncontrolled and uncontrollable tides of passion. It was, I think, his bitter resentment that within the university so many could be found to swim uncomplainingly with those tides that brought out all his latent forces of defiance and leadership.

Yet even in this phase he still counselled an appeal to reason rather than one to force, which he loathed. He would pace up and down my small attic-room, no palace even by student standards, making acid comments on the course of events and the stupidity and headstrongness of men.

'It's at times like this,' he said, 'that you see how thin civilization is. On the slightest pretext men willingly give up their powers of reason and act according to the instinct of self-preservation and the principle that might is right.' He made an expressive gesture that condemned all loose thinking. 'I suppose it's not surprising. After all the Age of Reason only began—when was it?—about three hundred years ago, I think. Three hundred years is only a small part of the time man has been trying to substitute his brain for his instincts, isn't it?'

I nodded. I do not think he noticed the nod. Nowadays he was indifferent to things like that. When he was trying to speak his thoughts, nothing else had any reality to him.

'But where is it going to end—where is it going to end?' he went on with the intensity of despair. 'Today, you mayn't study unless you wear a shirt of the right colour. That's only the beginning. Soon they'll be saying that you mustn't teach unless your shirt is right.'

'It can hardly come to that,' I protested.

His lip curled. 'Can't it? It'll be here very soon. And you can see where that's going to lead. A fact won't be a fact any more because you can prove it by experiment or logical reasoning. It'll only be a fact if it agrees with what *they* say. When that state is reached, God help us all!'

The Last Throw

'What can we do about it?' I asked not very helpfully. I was not indifferent to what was going on all round me—no one in the university could be. But my position was extremely delicate. I was not an Italian. For that reason I had to remain as aloof from it all as I possibly could. An 'undesirable alien' was a very easy target—especially one who, like me, had no recognized government to protect him. At any moment too, as anyone with knowledge of such movements as this could see, the heresy hunt might turn away from fellow-Italians towards foreigners, who are always good butts for partisan venom when all else fails.

Giovanni's face grew grave. 'Fight, George—fight till the end. No-one with any sense of decency or intellectual honesty can come to terms with a thing like this. It's an odd thought that the Renaissance began in Italy—and the knowledge and culture and freedom it produced may perish there.'

To be quite frank, I felt that Giovanni was growing a trifle too obsessed by these events and his sudden upsurge of interest in political struggle. The native is often the least competent judge of his compatriots' aims and actions, because he shares with them their virtues and their vices. I knew, as an outsider, the Italians for a warmhearted, friendly, and at times almost childlike people; but they were also sentimental, passionate, and excitable, and when these latter traits secured the upper hand they were carried away into excesses that, in their better moments, they would have abhorred. It was precisely there, too, that their childishness most revealed itself; for when their passion was spent, they would revert to their normal, likeable selves and not only forget their misdeeds but even fail to see that they merited any blame. These Fascist outrages, I felt—though I admit not very confidently—were a product of typical though perhaps unusually virulent Italian excess; sometime the reaction would come, and then all would return to normal.

I have never been a particularly shrewd judge of political events, and often I have been wrong in my estimates; but never was I more grievously mistaken than in that view. And never was Giovanni's judgement more swiftly confirmed. It was, I think, no more than a couple of days after that conversation that the official decree came: a purge of professors, lecturers, and demonstrators was to take place. Nor was there any of the mock leniency about it which had marked the orders affecting the students. Any of the latter not joining the official Party suffered no more than exclusion from various facilities—at any rate for the time being, though it was obvious that there were plenty of other means of punishment or coercion that could be applied. On the teachers the blow fell suddenly and with utter severity.

The first and obvious victims were those who had openly declared themselves opponents of Fascism, or even merely expressed their doubts of it—and, of course, avowed Socialists and Communists. These were instantly dismissed, without right of appeal and without any prospect of securing another appointment in Italy. It was these who formed the first wave of the flood of intellectual refugees who, later, were to add much to the cultural resources of the Western Democracies, particularly Britain, France, and the United States.

When these had gone, their places had to be filled. It was here that Giovanni's forebodings were strikingly fulfilled. The qualification was not professional or academic eminence, but political soundness. The ardour of their Fascism was of far more importance than their attainments as teachers. The first great crop of all bigotry—mediocrity —was already springing up lushly.

Next came the turn of those who had not expressed any sort of political bias—men in the main wrapped up in their work to whom politics seemed a strange and dangerous jungle into which it were wiser not to stray. Their choice was simple. They must become Fascists—or it would be assumed that they were traitors and enemies. Never was the principle of 'you are either for us or against us' more ruthlessly applied.

The Last Throw

Rather surprisingly to many of us, the majority accepted the grim alternative and bowed the knee to the New God in the Black Shirt.

I pointed this out to Giovanni. 'You're fighting a lost cause,' I remarked despondently and not a little anxiously, for the danger to him grew daily. 'More than half the teaching staff are Fascists, and that means that life for you anti-Fascists won't be worth living.'

'That may be so,' he replied acidly, 'but the certainty of defeat doesn't justify compromise. I'm not fighting Fascism as such. I'm neither pro or anti anything; life's too complicated for any clear-cut division like that. What I'm fighting for is intellectual honesty and freedom. If the Fascists will grant that—freedom for all to learn and speak—I won't oppose them.'

'Then there must be singularly little intellectual honesty in academic circles,' I observed.

'You mustn't be too hard on them, George,' he said softly, much to my surprise. 'Can you say that you wouldn't act as they have? I'm sure I couldn't. You see, we're only students. If we fail here,—well there are other things we can do. We're young anyway. But the bulk of these people aren't. Many of 'em are hoping to retire soon, and they've given all their lives to their work. They're too old to think of starting all over again. What's their choice? Obedience or starvation, isn't it? Maybe some of them would prefer starvation if only they themselves were concerned, but they've wives and families. No, George, we mustn't judge them too harshly.'

It was typical of him to perceive so clearly and even to sympathize with the human frailties and problems of those whose weakness he despised. That ability was one of the things which made him so implacable an enemy of the Fascist creed.

But if there was much conformity, that does not mean that there was no opposition. It came from the celebrated men—professors so eminent that even the Fascist juggernaut had to move carefully. Here were men whose reputation was international and whose victimization might well raise international protests—for which Fascism was barely strong enough. More than that, the Fascists knew that it was impossible to dispense with the services of these specialists; if they went, there was no-one to replace them from within the avowed supporters of the Party. Even the Fascists could not afford to reduce their whole system of higher education to a farce. Against such giants, the Fascists felt themselves at a disadvantage.

Professor Almarini—that is not his real name—was one of these resistors. Holding the Chair of Biochemistry at Florence, he was one of the world's greatest experts on nutrition and dietetics—and also one whose services the authorities at Rome most wanted to retain. For Mussolini was talking of raising the low standard of living among the Italian peasants and of using every scientific means to that end. It would have been a poor advertisement for this piece of window-dressing—it was no more—if it had been begun by the dismissal of an authority whose opinion was sought by governments and organizations all over the world on matters of nutrition.

He rejected the overtures made to him—and he did so contemptuously. Possessing that quality of intellectual honesty which Giovanni so much admired, he was also blunt. He told the Fascists that if they wanted his services he would continue to render them in the accustomed manner—but on his own terms, not on theirs. If they did not agree, then America, France, Britain—any country in the world—would welcome him with open arms and honour him. Nor was this any vain boast; it was the simple truth.

Probably, left to their own devices, the Fascist high authorities would have taken it at that and found some convenient formula to make it appear that no sacrifice of sacred principle was involved. But it is one of the inherent defects of dictatorial systems that they unleash forces which cannot be kept under full control. A mob majority indoctrinated into the belief that they have the right to impose their will on others by all manner of force and persecution are not likely to forgo these delights easily or to make exceptions in individual cases. Students led to believe that because they belong to a privileged class they are at liberty to assert their authority even against university discipline when the latter is suspect of dangerous tendencies are more likely to abuse their position than use it wisely. The student is never readily submissive to authority; if he is told he has the right—and indeed the duty—to flout it under certain conditions he will make the most of his opportunities.

Despite his stout refusals and his no less uncompromising comments, then, Professor Almarini was not removed from his Chair. Nor did he, as some of his similarly placed colleagues at other universities had, see a way out by devoting himself more to private research so as to reduce his appearances before students to the minimum. Rightly, Almarini believed that he had something of importance to say to his students that only he could say, and that it was his duty, while he still held the Chair, to say it. Accordingly he made no change whatever in his normal routine; his lectures proceeded according to the syllabus.

At first the plan seemed to be succeeding. It looked as though the aggressive Fascist students, who had not hesitated to express their disapproval in the most violent way of lesser figures, had taken the hint and were prepared to sink their prejudices as a tribute to the professor's eminence. But this was only a passing phase. Perhaps they expected some new ruling to reach them from above. Whatever the reason they showed nothing more than an insolent restiveness as if they regarded listening to such a monster of political blackness an insult to their finer feelings. Such self-control could not last indefinitely. The habit of persecution is a drug that demands constant indulgence. The upshot was a crisis in the career not only of Professor Almarini, but also of my friend Giovanni Campo; and as this is his story that is the more important point.

The Last Throw

There were signs of a gathering storm as soon as we entered the lecture theatre. It was packed. Almarini's lectures were naturally always well attended, but I had never seen the hall so crowded before. More significant, it was no ordinary audience of students in nondescript and varied garb. The overwhelming majority of those present were wearing the black shirt and breeches of the Fascist Party, and it was obvious that their mob determination was high. Something about their expressions suggested the cruel expectancy of a pack of hounds following a good scent.

Amid a deep silence, the professor entered. That silence was a tribute neither to his eminence nor to his masterful personality, which had never so far failed to subdue the most unruly pack of students; it was a threat and at the same time a promise of evil to come. But he took no notice. So far as his mien went, the unusual sight of students in Fascist uniforms might have been the most commonplace of experiences. In his usual way he arranged his notes, took the preparatory sip of water he always allowed himself, and began. . . .

No-one took notes. The lecture was an important one dealing with some aspects of recent original researches, but not even the non-Fascist students paid much attention. The air was thick with foreboding, and learning was far from everyone's thoughts.

Someone started to boo. The noise ran round the hall like wind rustling through corn. Almarini paused, waited for it to subside, and then resumed as though nothing had happened. Again the boo began, rose, died away; and again the professor paused and recommenced. Steadily the storm grew. Catcalls, insults, and every manner of noise, were added to the mounting din. Almarini stood there, his face expressionless; only the tightening grip of his hands as he held them clasped in front of him testified to his own growing nervous tension. Then, slowly, there spread across his features a look of utter contempt.

Nothing could have been better calculated to rouse all the worst in these hooligans. Rage—hysterics—threats:

these they could have understood; and perhaps if Almarini had reacted in one of those ways the incident would have closed for the time being. But that expression of contempt, conveying as it did his opinion of them, was something they could not grasp. No man had the right to despise them—especially this non-juring professor. Were they not the élite of the country, the Party in whom all truth and power—particularly power—resided?

The clamour began to take a more ominous note. It was no longer confined to inarticulate sounds of disapproval. Words started to fill the air.

'Resign!'—'Traitor!'—'Go before we make you, you dog!' These were the kind of expressions that were hurled at Almarini, who stood still quietly and rigidly, though his eye was beginning to glow with the rage that he concealed and would not reveal to please the mob.

I glanced at Giovanni, sitting a little distance away with a group of students, whose ordinary clothes were almost startling amid all those uniforms. He was white and drawn, but I saw the danger sign—the narrowing of the mouth and the little twitch at the corners. Even as I looked, I saw him give a faint nod. In a moment the anti-Fascist students were on their feet.

'Traitors yourselves!' they yelled in unison.

It was a challenge that the Fascists could not ignore. For the moment, Almarini's cold contempt had puzzled them; they were at a loss to know how to carry the demonstration further. The anti-Fascist students' action gave them just the chance they needed. Abandoning their attack on the professor, they turned on the protesters, and in a second the room became a battlefield. Nothing in all the long series of past students' fights had been the equal of this. The Fascists were sure of themselves now; they were bosses and knew it; and they were out for blood. Nor were they troubled about rules of decency. They used their boots as readily as their fists and it went ill with any student who was knocked to the ground; he was not merely trampled upon but kicked senseless.

The Last Throw

There are times when pride is a danger and discretion is, in truth, the better part of valour. It would have been well if the professor had recognized these facts. He would have been wise to have retreated while the mob was otherwise engaged. As it was he stood like a statue, some strange god presiding over a rite of combat.

The temper of the Fascists was now beyond the semblance of control. They turned from their student enemies, whom they outnumbered by perhaps ten to one and who had no chance at all, and rushed threateningly on Almarini. He did not flinch as they began to jostle and push him, nor did he make any resistance. And then a cry rang out:

'Death to the traitor!'

There was a moment's silence as though this suggestion was too much even for these hooligans and that its enormity had awakened them to a sense of what they were doing. It was only a temporary pause; in a minute the cry was taken up and one burly student seized the professor's arms and twisted them behind his back.

At that moment Giovanni leapt forward. Never before had I seen him in that mood. His face was white with rage and his eyes burned with passion. He seemed to wind up his body like a spring, and then he crashed a blow into the tormentor's face that sent the latter reeling and gasping against the wall.

'Run!' he hissed to the professor. And Almarini, his calm shattered at last, fled.

Giovanni turned to face the Fascists. His face was a mask of hatred and anger, but there was also a strange light now in his eyes as though he was already contemplating death. For after what he had done he knew there would be no mercy. The Fascists had been robbed of their prey, and he, Giovanni, was the robber. His fists raised, he backed against the wall. If he was to die, he was going to die bravely and without surrender.

Death would certainly have come to him if he had been left alone. Yet his courage and determination had rallied his beaten supporters. They could not stand by and see him cruelly beaten to death by this animal pack; and reforming themselves into a phalanx they thrust their way to his side, hitting about them with any weapon that came to hand. It was no time for fists; they had to use every poor advantage they could seize.

A forlorn hope, indeed; yet it succeeded through sheer courage. The Fascists were taken by surprise, for they had thought the students utterly routed. They fell back a little, and into the space poured the young men who were now rescuing the rescuer.

Giovanni smiled very faintly, but he did not move. Not far away was a door, for the moment unprotected, and he tried, by word and gesture, to make his followers escape through it while he faced the enemy. They would have none of it. It was Giovanni's turn to take orders; and they were of the kind that could not be disobeyed.

'Run!' said one of the students—his name, I believe, was Enrico. It was the advice Giovanni had given to the professor. 'And don't show your face here again.'

For the briefest moment Giovanni hesitated. He hated flight, even more perhaps than the professor had, for Giovanni was now an active enemy of Fascism. A final push persuaded him. A minute later he had leapt through the door, which the student slammed behind him and guarded.

Giovanni was gone, where I did not know, though it was clear the university would know him no more. That blow had been his last desperate stroke, his final declaration of his passion for freedom, and it had sealed his fate. It drove Professor Almarini to a foreign land, where he was honoured and respected; for Giovanni it opened the gate to strange paths and a life of obscurity in far places.

Chapter Four

THE FUGITIVE

My room, as I have already hinted, was neither large nor luxurious. On the contrary, it can only be described by the word 'attic', which I do not seek to divest of all its somewhat sordid overtones. But it was convenient, served my not very exacting needs, and, above all, was the cheapest I could find. If there had been one cheaper, I should have found it; but there was not. It was, therefore, not a place in which I did any entertaining or indeed invited visitors, though a few intimates, among them Giovanni Campo, occasionally found their way there. Others, even if they located the house, were likely to be discouraged by the long and trying ascent by way of rickety, ill-lit, and uncovered wooden stairs.

A visitor at any hour was, then, something of an event for me. But a visitor just after midnight was something beyond all imagination. Yet on that night after the affair of Professor Almarini there was a knock at my door. I was expecting no-one. The landlord was not likely to disturb me at that hour. The wildest thoughts ran through my head. An atmosphere of terror was already poisoning the peaceful atmosphere of Florence, and the tales of midnight arrests and questionings were too numerous and too circumstantial to be dismissed as rumours. Men disappeared from their beds, were hauled from the very arms of their wives, and never heard of again. The disappearance of an insignificant medical student from an attic would not be noticed, and the only person to remark it with regret would be the landlord, whose weekly rent fell due the next day.

All kinds of terrifying thoughts rushed through my head, as I stood hesitating whether to answer the knock or not. Foremost in my mind was that I had been present at the fight that afternoon, and, though I had, with difficulty, refrained from joining in it, even when Giovanni was threatened, it would be easy enough to implicate me if the Fascists so desired. I was Giovanni's friend; therefore I must share his sympathies (the Fascist mind cannot understand that antitheses of outlook may dwell together in peace); and if they could not get Giovanni's blood they might as well have mine.

So I stood, almost unable to move, frightened more by my reflections than by the unknown visitor to whom I had not yet opened my door. The knock came again, rather louder, and I made a hesitating step towards the door. Holding out would only make things worse for me; I knew that I could not hope that the unknown would go away. Eventually the door would be broken down, and then, no doubt, I should be beaten and tortured for resisting investigation. Slowly, reluctantly, apprehensively, I opened the door.

But it was no band of Fascist desperadoes who stood on the threshold. Rather puzzled, I stared at the visitor, whom I did not recognize. He stood with head cast down. His clothes were torn, tattered, and blood-stained; indeed, a small trickle of blood oozed slowly down his leg, clearly visible through the tatters. His arms were crossed over his lower chest, with the shoulders dropped—the characteristic attitude of a man in considerable pain.

'Yes?' I said. 'What is it?'

I was still puzzled, but no longer scared. This battered specimen of humanity could harm no one. Probably, I thought, he is someone who has fallen foul of the Fascists and, unable to afford a doctor, had come to see if my prentice hand could attend to his ills—a petty thief, it might be, who did not want to draw too much attention to himself. There were plenty of that kind in the neighbourhood in which I lived.

Slowly he raised his head, as though the effort cost him much. I gasped. It was Giovanni!

Quickly I put my arm round him and helped him to my rickety bed, on which I laid him. He walked with a curious motion as though he had pebbles in his shoes. There was no need to ask questions. The truth was obvious. Already the Fascists had taken some toll for his part in the afternoon's riots.

He saw that I understood and nodded.

'Don't try to talk,' I said. 'Just lie there quietly and rest. I'll see to you.'

I may not have been a properly qualified doctor, but I knew what to do in his case. I ripped his clothes off him; it was an easy thing to do, for there was practically nothing left of them; and the more I revealed of his body, the more terrible his condition appeared.

His face was bleeding from a dozen wounds and scratches, as though he had been clawed by some gigantic cat. His back was swollen and red, though there was little lividity and no weals: I guessed that he had been beaten with a rubber truncheon. There were the same signs, too, on his feet. On his left thigh was a nasty gash, which still bled.

While I dressed his wounds and did what I could to make him comfortable, the kettle boiled. I made him coffee, and when he had gently and with difficulty taken a cup, he smiled slightly and pathetically.

'Yes, George, they got me,' he said. 'There was nowhere else I could come. I'm sorry. But I don't think I was followed. It's safe for the time being.'

'Don't talk if it tires you,' I advised. Anxious as I was to hear his story, I was no less concerned to show that I knew my job.

'That's all right, George,' he whispered. 'I'd rather talk. Makes it easier and takes my mind off the aches and pains for a bit.'

'That's all right, then,' I said. 'Where did they find you?'

He smiled ruefully. 'Where they expected to—at home,' he replied. 'I was a darned fool. I rambled about for a long time after I left the university, you see,' he went on, 'mingling with crowds as much as possible. I didn't think they'd send out an S.O.S. for me and I thought that'd be safe. My plan was to wait for nightfall and then try to get right away somewhere—I didn't mind where.'

'Yes,' I said. 'Sure all this isn't distressing you?'

He shook his head—and grimaced. 'That hurts,' he remarked. 'But I wanted to go back to my room first to get a few things, and that's how I fell into it. I worked my way back soon after nightfall—and the first thing I saw was a Blackshirt standing outside the house, obviously on guard. So I retired. I came back several times, and he was still there, and after the sixth attempt I was on the point of giving it up. Then a funny thing happened. Another Blackshirt came along and the two had a discussion. After a little while, they glanced up at my window, nodded to each other, and went off together. I thought they must have decided to give it up as useless, so as soon as they were out of sight I broke cover and simply flew up to my room.'

'And then they came back and caught you?' I suggested.

He nodded. 'Yes,' he replied. 'It was a trap, I suppose. They realized I wouldn't show my face with that chap pacing about outside, so they must have taken him off and then watched. I'd barely been in the room ten minutes before I heard feet on the stairs and people arguing. It was the Fascists all right—the argument was my landlady protesting. She was still at it when I opened the door—I didn't want them to break in; and then they got tired of her and one of them just led her to the top of the stairs and pushed her down. Luckily it's only a short flight, that last one that leads to my attic, so I don't think she was badly hurt.'

He paused for breath, and I refilled his coffee cup. After he had taken a few sips, he was ready to continue.

'Yes, it was a pretty bad business altogether. There were six of them, and I hadn't a chance. They bundled me off, after having looked at the things I'd gathered together. It wasn't much, but there were a few things of some value in it—my watch, some money, and odds and ends like that. They pocketed all that, of course. I'd no right to any property.'

Up to now he had sounded weary, and his voice had been monotonous. But with that last ironic sentence there was an echo of the incisive voice I knew so well. Whatever he had gone through had not changed him.

'I was blindfolded and when I was allowed to see again I found myself in some horrible damp cellar,' he resumed. 'The room seemed full of those Blackshirts, and it looked as though they were going to enjoy themselves. But they started off by trying to sound very reasonable.'

'That sounds almost incredible,' I remarked.

'Well, that's what happened, though it was only window-dressing. Even if I'd agreed to their proposals, I think I should have got what I did later. Maybe not quite so severe, but bad enough.'

'What were their proposals?'

'They told me I'd acted in a perfectly damnable way, and that these things were no affair of mine as I wasn't a member of the Party, and university discipline, whether it was applied to professors or students, was now in their hands. But of course, they went on, if I wanted to concern myself with university affairs the way was open to me.'

'Joining the Party, I suppose they meant,' I commented.

'More than that. I could join the Party and go on probation for a little while, and I was to make a public apology for my behaviour before the entire university and instruct all who had supported me that they must follow my example—except for the public apology.'

'And,' I asked, rather needlessly, 'you refused?'

'Of course.'

'So they started their parlour tricks then?'

'Not for a little while. They argued with me, and they were good enough to say that I had certain qualities they would like to see used in the services of the Party.' His tone of scorn was deadly. 'I still refused, so they started to get busy.'

'Don't talk about it if you don't want to,' I reminded him.

'It doesn't make any difference,' he replied. 'They were well provided. There were dozens of rubber truncheons about—or that's how it seemed to me—and they'd other nice little things, like small wire whips. They account for my face, by the way,' he added almost casually.

'I wondered what had caused all those wounds.' They looked like scratches but they quite obviously weren't when you looked at them closely.

He paused for a moment broodingly, as though reliving those agonizing moments. Suddenly he looked at me.

'You've never been beaten on the soles of your feet with a rubber truncheon, have you, George?' he asked softly.

I shook my head violently. 'No; and I never want to be,' I answered.

'You're right—it's unadulterated hell,' he said. 'You can stand it on your shoulders and your chest and your bottom and your arms, though that's bad enough. But on the feet——' He drew a deep breath. 'I know now why the eastern people feared the bastinado so much.'

'I can well understand that,' I observed, though I knew that no-one can judge the quality of a pain unless he has experienced it himself.

'In the end, I think, they got a little tired of it all, as they didn't succeed in getting anything out of me in the way of a promise or apology. One of them even suggested I'd better be disposed of, but the others shook their heads. "Not yet", one of the bosses said. "Give him a chance to see wisdom," and so they decided to let me go after they'd administered the last corrective for my evil ways.'

'What's that?' I asked.

'Castor oil,' he replied promptly. 'That was the one thing

that really upset me. I was not going to take castor oil,' he went on emphatically. 'I'd made up my mind about that, but I didn't see how I was going to get out of it. They were about fifteen to one, I suppose, and I'd a lot taken out of me, as you can see, so I wasn't in a good position for resistance. Then luck helped me. I told you they'd got tired of me—they even forgot me. Two of them were fumbling about with the castor-oil bottle and the others looked on making silly schoolboy jokes, and one of them had even left his cosh within my reach. They'd let go my arms, too. I just fastened on to that cosh like a leech—they didn't even notice it. And that wasn't all—just at that moment, while I was trying to think out the best way of escape, one of them went out of the room— and he left the door unlocked and slightly ajar. They probably thought I couldn't even walk after their bastinadoing, and they were quite entitled to that belief.'

'Go on,' I said, forgetting my role as medical attendant and becoming absorbed in his story.

'Of course, I forgot all about the pains in my feet and made a bolt for it. It took them off their guard, but one of them sprang towards me and tried to cut me off. I let him have it. I just brought that rubber cosh down with a crash on his head, and he sank to the floor. Few things have ever given me so much pleasure.'

In all Giovanni's astonishing story—none the less astonishing because I knew every word of it to be true and understatement rather than an exaggeration—nothing was more breathtaking than that last remark. That Giovanni should find delight in being brutal to a fellow human being was almost beyond belief. But the glint in his eye and the set of his mouth showed that even now he was recalling the incident with satisfaction, to say the least.

'I never thought I'd be able to walk at more than a hobble,' he continued. 'But it's wonderful what you can do when it's a choice between escape and that sort of thing.

The Fugitive

I ran as hard as I could. I didn't know where I was going, and I didn't know what I might run into. They'd probably shoot if they saw me. But actually I only ran into one Blackshirt, and he was so astonished at seeing me that I had no difficulty in giving him the cosh, too, before he could raise the alarm.'

'Luck was on your side,' I commented.

'It was indeed. I could see daylight, and I ran towards it and found an open door. Once I was in the street and round a corner, I slackened my pace a bit. For one thing, my feet were hurting like mad. For another I wanted to get my bearings. I kept a bright look out for pursuit, ready to make off at the slightest sound, but apparently they'd had enough for the time being. Anyway, no-one followed me, so far as I know. It was then I discovered the benefits of insomnia.'

I gazed at this remarkable man, who related such extraordinary experiences in so matter-of-fact a way, and felt that these same experiences must have upset his mind a little.

'Insomnia?' I gasped.

'Yes,' he replied, with a ghost of a smile. 'Insomnia. You see, George, for some time I've suffered from insomnia of a kind. In spite of all we learn, I've a horror of doping myself, and I've discovered that the best cure is to take a long walk just before going to bed and make myself absolutely physically exhausted. I've been doing that for quite a time now, and I suppose I've explored every back street in Florence in the process. More than that, I've come to know what places look like late at night. So I recognized at once where I was, and by taking a series of short cuts I got here in about half the time it would have taken me by the obvious route. Moreover I think my zig-zagging would have put them completely off the scent.'

'You're a most remarkable person, Giovanni,' I remarked. 'What happens now?'

'Can you put me up?' he asked. 'I know it's a hell of a lot to ask and I won't blame you if you refuse. I know you're a foreigner and have to be careful not to be mixed up in this beastly business. But I don't think they have the faintest idea where I've gone, and I'm probably not important enough to chase. What I've had will satisfy them for the time being.'

'Yes,' I said doubtfully. The thoughts I had had when hearing his knock at my door recurred to me. 'On the other hand, they know I'm your closest friend, and this would be an obvious place to look. They might think I had information they could beat out of me.'

His expression grew serious. 'I hadn't thought of that,' he remarked. 'I was too anxious to get somewhere where I knew I could get a bit of rest to think it all out. No, it wouldn't be safe for you. Give me some clothes then, and I'll get away as soon as I can walk a bit.'

I looked at him, and a strange feeling came over me. I grew ashamed and despised myself. How could I allow my own personal safety to stand in the way of helping this young man who had already suffered so much for his ideals and beliefs and was clearly quite ready to suffer more and expose himself to new risks, without a thought for himself? There was, too, the practical point that he dared not appear in public in his present state, and I was quite ready to find that when his present mood of excitement wore off and reaction set in, he would find himself very weak. It was impossible.

'No,' I said, a little mendaciously. 'I was thinking of your safety more than mine. If they catch me or question me, I shall know nothing—rest assured of that. But if they come here and find you, it'll be terrible. This room is too small to hide a mouse, let alone a man who can barely walk and ought to lie down the whole time.'

'I shouldn't have come here,' he muttered. 'I'm sorry, George, really sorry, but——'

'Stop!' I broke in with a firm gesture. 'Of course you did right to come here. I should be a poor friend if I couldn't help you just when you most need help, shouldn't I? After all, there's nothing much they can do to me. They can beat me, but they're as likely to do that because I'm a foreigner as for anything else. I'm ready to take whatever risk there is if you are.'

'You're a real friend, George,' he said earnestly. 'I knew you wouldn't let me down, but you're right to think of all the risks.'

'All right, then,' I said with as business-like an air as I could assume. 'You stay here till you're well. What then?'

For a few minutes he was silent. It was difficult to make him out for he had an air almost of embarrassment.

'Have you got something in mind?' I asked.

'Yes,' he replied with a shamefaced air. 'I hardly like to ask you, George, after all your kindness in agreeing to let me stay here.'

'Tell me,' I insisted. 'Something has got to be done, and I can think of nothing at the moment. If you've a plan of any kind and I can help you, then let's examine it at least.'

'You remember Lydia, George—Lydia Buonsanti?' he asked.

I nodded slowly. Yes, of course I remembered Lydia. Giovanni and I had been together when the girl was introduced to us at one of the social gatherings organized by the university. From the very first, she and Giovanni had obviously been attracted. The daughter of a well-known and wealthy trader of the town, she was tall, dark, handsome and vivacious, with all the natural gay charm of the Italian girl of twenty-one. The reserved strength and shyness of Giovanni was, I think, a new experience for her, very different from the attentions she received from almost every aspiring young man in Florence, who saw in her the possibility of a wife who was both rich and beautiful. Giovanni was nothing of the cavalier; he tended rather, in his solitary, self-contained way, to avoid girls. But with Lydia he was at his ease at once, and I had rarely seen him so animated as during that first conversation with her.

From that moment, the two had started to go about

together a great deal. If there was some function at the university, Lydia was always Giovanni's lady guest. They went to cafés together. Sometimes they invited me, and I could not help noticing once or twice the graceful way in which she, to whom money meant little, contrived to pay a bill that would have strained both Giovanni's and my own resources to the utmost.

I liked Lydia, most of all when she was speaking, with a light in her eye, of Giovanni. 'He is so good and so different,' she had said to me once. 'In these days, it is so refreshing to meet a man who is determined to make a career not so much for his own advantage as to provide benefits for others. He will be a great doctor some day'.

Yes, I knew Lydia. But how did she come into the picture?

'I want you to go and see her as early as you can to-morrow morning,' Giovanni resumed, breaking in on my recollections. 'She likes me, George, and one day, perhaps, when all these troubles are over and I have something tangible to offer her, we may get married. I love her, George, not only for herself but also because she shares my ideals and thinks as I do. But I do not think Signor Buonsanti would welcome a poor medical student as a prospective son-in-law—least of all one who's been beaten up by the Blackshirts.'

'What do you want me to do, then?' I asked, checking these sentimental remarks.

'See her alone, George. I am sure she will find some way of helping me and getting me away from Florence. Her father is on the council, and a passenger in one of his cars wouldn't be challenged by the Fascists. But whether it's that or some other way, she will help. At any rate, she must know what has happened. I should be meeting her tonight,' he added sadly.

'Do you think you ought to involve her in all this?' I asked doubtfully.

'She would be offended if I did not ask her help,' replied Giovanni stoutly. 'I am sure of it. She thinks my thoughts and hates this kind of tyranny. Will you do it for me George—please?'

I nodded without enthusiasm, for I had grave misgivings. I did not doubt Giovanni's estimate of his fair Lydia. Between them, as I had seen for myself, was a quite remarkable sympathy, and I could not imagine that a girl in her position would waste her time on a poor man like Giovanni unless she had something more than a passing interest in him. Lydia, then, I did not doubt. But I was considerably dubious of the wisdom of calling on her, in the early hours of the day, at her home on such an errand.

I was unknown to the servants. My coming at such an hour as he proposed—seven o'clock was what he had mentioned—would inevitably attract comment. Besides, she had her father's position to consider. He was a prominent citizen, and though I knew nothing of his political affiliations, I did realize that, whether Fascist or anti-Fascist, he would not welcome, either for his own sake or for hers, any involvement in the political cauldron of the university.

Rather diffidently I put some of these points to Giovanni, who listened attentively, but with obvious disagreement.

'You are a careful man, George,' he said, 'and I do appreciate your thoughtfulness, especially so far as it safeguards Lydia. But the difficulties you mention do not exist. I expect Luigi will answer the door to you—you will have no difficulty with him. He is always most helpful. And as for Lydia, she is an independent girl, and her father lets her go her own way very much. But I repeat, George, she ought to know even if she decides she cannot help. I don't think it will come to that, for at least she will suggest a way, even if she can do nothing on her own. Will you go, George?'

I looked at him. He had changed again, and I was getting a glimpse of yet another aspect of Giovanni's character. He was pleading with an almost child-like intensity, so as to give me the feeling of being an unnecessarily harsh and unreasonable parent. After all he should be the better judge than I of the situation. Moreover there was no alternative plan to consider as yet. It was this or nothing; and one thing was certain: the sooner Giovanni left my attic the better it would be for him and for my own peace of mind.

'All right,' I said at last. 'If you are convinced that it is the best thing to do, I will do it. I won't disguise from you that it's not something I shall enjoy, and I shall be glad when it's over. But it's an unpleasant situation altogether, and we must make the best of it and do what we can to ease it.'

'Thank you, George, thank you. You are the best of friends.'

The reaction was already beginning to set in, and he was almost asleep. His voice was a drowsy drawl. I drew the bedclothes over him—they were not very magnificent; nothing was in that room—and in a few moments he was in deep slumber.

My watch told me it was half-past one. In less than six hours I must be out on my unattractive errand. Settling myself in the one chair my room boasted and propping my feet on the small, shaky table, I decided to get whatever rest I might.

Chapter Five

THE DENIAL

I awoke with a crick in my neck and an aching body and for a bewildered moment I was unable to remember what had happened or why I had been sleeping so uncomfortably when there was a bed in the room. The sound of heavy, troubled breathing brought all back with a rush. Giovanni Campo had been beaten up. More than that I had promised to see Lydia Buonsanti for him as early as I possibly could. Anxiously wondering whether I had slept too late, I glanced at my watch. It was just after six o'clock. If I stirred myself now, washed, and made myself as presentable as I could, I might be just in time.

The Buonsantis' house was in one of the richer districts of the town, which it would take me a little while to reach. I knew the way, for I had been there on one occasion with Giovanni. As I proceeded along the streets, taking as many short cuts as I knew (for the holder of a guilty secret believes he is suspected even when no-one notices him), I reflected on this mission I had undertaken; and the more I thought about it, the less I liked it. There were danger and suspicion everywhere; one never knew where one was safe or among friends; even husbands could no longer trust their wives nor wives their husbands, so evil was the spirit of this Fascism that was pervading the fair land of Italy. Not that I doubted Lydia personally. What I feared was that our conversation might be overheard and Giovanni betrayed by some eavesdropping servant—and in those days every servant was a potential spy and informer. The best thing, I reflected, Giovanni and I could have done was to maintain silence, and take no-one else into our risky secret. No doubt we could have evolved some means of escape for him, and then it would have been wise to inform Lydia. To drag her in at this stage was a move, I believed with ever-increasing conviction, that was fraught with additional and unnecessary dangers for everyone. Once or twice I was on the point of turning back and returning to Giovanni with the purpose of discussing it all over again. But I knew it would be useless. His mind was made up; and when he had made a decision of that kind he was unshakable. My word had been pledged and I must carry it out, no matter what the cost in inconvenience and misgivings.

At last I found myself outside the Buonsantis' house. It was large, prosperous-looking, and aloof—not at all the sort of house, I felt, that would welcome being disturbed at this unconventional hour. That impression and the knowledge that my mission was not a straightforward one of which I could give any reasonable account to a stranger made me want to tiptoe across the patio to the door.

My first ring produced no response, and with some trepidation I rang again. I waited with rising hopes; if I could get no answer my promise was redeemed without untoward consequences; but they sank again when, after a short pause, I heard the sound of footsteps within. The door was thrown open and revealed a tall, slim manservant regarding me with that air of respectful insolence which the servants of the rich, the world over, reserve for poor callers. And instantly (as was intended) I became acutely aware of the shabbiness of my clothes and the unsuitability of the hour. He did not speak but raised his eyebrows interrogatively.

'May I speak to Signorina Buonsanti?' I asked.

The eyebrows were raised a little higher—this time in surprise.

'The signorina is not yet up,' he replied. 'Who is it wishes to see her?'

I gave my name, adding that I had an important

message for her from the university, which I wished to deliver before beginning my day's work there. This seemed to me a good gambit, for Lydia's family took a great interest in the life of the university, with which they were closely connected, and also gave some sort of explanation for my early call.

The man shrugged slightly. If this was the helpful Luigi, he was not extending to me the favours he apparently granted to Giovanni.

'If there is a message I can deliver it to her,' he said brusquely.

My temper was beginning to rise. I knew that if I had been fashionably clad and had arrived in one of those beautiful sports cars that the younger well-to-do Italians had made their own—even if I had a few lire to distribute —my reception would have been very different. But I knew also that Italian menservants, like their kind in all countries, are at heart bullies and cowards, ever ready to be insolent to those whom they see no reason to fear, but ready to crawl the moment they are kicked.

'Tell the signorina I am here,' I snapped, so suddenly that he started. 'Give her my name, and ask if she will see me now or would prefer me to call later.'

The sharp, commanding tone worked. The man almost grovelled.

'Yes, signor—at once, signor. Perhaps you will be good enough to wait in here.'

He showed me into a little room. Its interior did not raise my hopes of a successful interview. This was the room of a wealthy family—and wealthy families were likely to want to do nothing to offend the dominant power. On the wall was a single Italian Primitive whose genuineness even I could recognize. There was not a knick-knack that did not speak of the combination, more common in Italy than in England, of wealth and taste. More ominous still, on a small occasional table lay copies of four or five of those newspapers which most strongly supported the Fascist cause.

The minutes drew on till I began to wonder if I was to be left here until my patience was exhausted and I let myself out, defeated. But after about twenty minutes of anxious waiting I heard steps approaching and the man reappeared. His temporary mood of respect had vanished; he was now plainly rude, having, no doubt, assured himself that I was the type of visitor on whom not even the semblance of respect should be wasted.

'The signorina is much inconvenienced,' he said curtly. 'But she will see you. Come this way.'

I followed him, this time into another small room, but fitted out as a study or writing-room on the first floor, and, after another five minutes' wait or so, the door opened to admit Lydia Buonsanti.

This was by no means the Lydia whom I knew. She was clothed in a handsome wrapper of the kind that is now known as a housecoat, though at that time I do not think it had risen to the dignity of a proper title. Her face was cold and distant. Her black hair, drawn back from her forehead, instead of being worn loosely, as was her wont, revealed what I had never noticed before—that her features were hard and her mouth rather cruel, especially as it was now, drawn into a thin, contemptuous line.

'This is a very remarkable hour to call, signor,' she said coldly. 'I hope that your message is sufficiently urgent to justify your intrusion.'

'I apologize deeply, signorina,' I replied abasing myself and taking her hint by the use of 'signor' in place of my name that she did not wish to claim any friendship with me. 'I should not have the courage to call at this hour but for the fact that I have a very urgent message from a close friend of yours.'

'Well?' she asked. My words aroused no sign of interest or curiosity in her.

'I come from Giovanni—Giovanni Campo,' I began, but she checked me. 'Perhaps it would be better not to say anything further,' she interjected, narrowing her eyes slightly.

I took this for a warning to be cautious. Perhaps, after all, she was playing for safety. Her coldness—her refusal to acknowledge me in a friendly way—might all be part of an elaborate precaution against spying by servants. My opinion of Luigi was certainly not that held by Giovanni, and I certainly would not have put eavesdropping above him.

I lowered my voice to a whisper. 'He is in great trouble,' I went on. 'He sent me to let you know about it. There was a fight in the university yesterday, and last night he was beaten up by the Fascists. He is in a very terrible state, signorina. He wished you to know about it, and I think perhaps he had an idea you might be able to help him.'

Even now she retained her coldness.

'It is very regrettable news, signor,' she said in a low voice that could, however, be clearly heard, and indicated no desire for secrecy. 'I am sorry to hear it. But why Giovanni Campo should send you here at this hour to tell me, I do not know. He must surely have been aware that his recent conduct in the university must sooner or later bring trouble upon himself in these troublous times. I am sorry, signor, that he has put you to this inconvenience. You may express my sympathy for his physical sufferings.'

Despite the formality of her words, there was a significant undertone that I could not miss. Lydia had already heard the news that I had brought her—and she was not interested. Her next words confirmed this belief, amounting to a conviction, of mine.

'Since Signor Campo,' she continued, 'has been so good as to send you to me with this message, I had better send one in reply. It is simply that I have no wish to be further involved in his affairs. A loyal citizen cannot become embroiled in revolutionary activities.'

It sounded as if she had carefully rehearsed that little speech of dismissal; nothing could have been further from her normal mode of speaking. I hesitated for a moment, at a loss what to say.

'I must ask you to go, Signor Sava,' she said pointedly.

'I am sure you will agree that I have been indulgent in granting you this interview. I do not wish to remain alone with a man at this hour of the morning while my parents are still asleep.'

She pressed a bellpush, and Luigi appeared almost at once, as though he had been waiting outside the door for the summons.

'Show Signor Sava out, Luigi,' she said.

'Certainly, signorina,' said Luigi, bowing. He gave me a glance that suggested he would rather kick than show me off the premises.

Slowly I made my way back to the attic, my thoughts forming a whirling, disordered pattern. I did not know how I was going to report this interview to Giovanni. That was going to be a painful process, both for him and for me. My message would be a double blow to him. In the first place, there was no hope of any help from Lydia. That was something to which he might reconcile himself. But also I had to convey her dismissal of him. She wanted nothing more to do with him—not even any news. That was a shock for which he was certainly not prepared. It was useless to try and make a plan of action; the best thing would be to let circumstances decide how to handle the situation.

How far did this attitude of Lydia's represent her true feelings? That was a question the answer to which completely eluded me. These were times in which the expression of an honest opinion on anything was a dangerous and chancy business. Already everyone was learning the value of playing safe, and since few casual human remarks are entirely free of ambiguity, an unaccustomed silence had descended upon the Italian people. Lydia might simply be anxious to avoid trouble—disastrous trouble—for both herself and her family; she could only do so by denying all connexion with Giovanni. But I had an uneasy feeling that it went deeper than a mere desire to put herself on the right side of authority. Her expression had barely altered from that of cold disdain during the whole of our meeting, and I did not think her a good enough actress to suppress all indications of her true feelings. Moreover, she had obviously been already informed of what had happened to Giovanni—and that argued some pretty close association with sources of Fascist information, for the Fascists did not openly proclaim the names of their latest victims. She might even be an active agent of the Party, in which case Giovanni's danger would be increased a hundredfold by this unfortunate affair. I recalled the look she had given me on parting—that look of vicious hate of which only Southern Europeans know the complete secret.

By now I was at the mouth of the shabby street in which I had my room. I felt reluctant to go further, for I wished to delay having to break the news for as long as I could. Yet I could not leave Giovanni alone. Our secret was no longer ours alone; and a secret shared with people, like Lydia, of unknown sympathies was a secret no longer. The Fascists might arrive, determined to complete the work they had begun on their implacable enemy, Giovanni Campo. He needed rest and food, and he was barely capable of looking after himself as yet. In any event, I had to get it over, and the sooner the better.

He looked up eagerly as I entered, his eyes searching my face for an answer before I spoke. I can remember still that almost childlike look of trustful hope as he stared at me—and I remember, too, how my heart sank, making my task seem doubly unpleasant.

'Tell me, George,' he said quickly. 'What did she say?'

I told him as briefly as I could without any evasions or half-truths, but trying to break the force of the blow as much as possible. Anxiously I waited to see the effect upon him.

For a minute or so he lay back on the bed as though stunned, his brows knitted and the corners of his mouth drooping, almost as though he did not quite comprehend the truth. Then he sat up slowly, his expression thoughtful.

'You were right, George,' he said in a surprisingly quiet voice. 'I ought never to have put her in such a position.

The Denial

Of course, the risk for her would be far too much—she could not take it. I shall never forgive myself for this. Never. I ought to have thought of all this. There are spies everywhere—one can barely trust one's own brother. And I owe you an apology, George—it must have been very unpleasant for you. I should never have submitted you to the ordeal.'

'Oh, that doesn't matter,' I remarked, astounded at his attitude. I had expected some sort of violent revulsion. Lydia had been his fiancée in all but the final formal sense; they had even spoken of their intended marriage while I had been with them and had certainly made no secret of their plans. To have all those schemes ruined in this way might well have reduced a man to the verge of breakdown. Not so Giovanni. His was a different temperament—one that was unwilling to see the bad in any human being yet ever ready to see the good. If anyone was to blame for a situation, Giovanni would first instinctively try to make himself responsible before attempting to judge anyone else. If it is a fine trait for a man to have in his character, it is also full of danger, for it will often blind him to the infidelities, treachery, and dishonesty of others. Controlled now by his own deep love for Lydia, he could not see the slightest suspicious circumstance in her behaviour, and if I had so much as whispered one of my own doubts, I am sure I would have roused him to violent anger.

So I kept my own misgivings to myself—misgivings that increased the more I reflected on the affair. More and more clearly Lydia emerged in my mind as a girl set entirely on her own ends, without the depth or strength of character to share the misfortunes, far less the dangers, of one she had professed to love. She was cold, calculating, and, with it all, superficial. No doubt the brilliant young student who was so different from the rest and before whom opened the promise of a magnificent career in medicine, had appealed to her. He was not one among many but a unique specimen—and she, like her father or mother in furnishing the house, as I had seen, was a collector of unique specimens. But it went no further than that.

Perhaps I misjudged her. Perhaps the immense force of circumstances which were driving thousands—millions—of Italians to perform acts and make statements alien to their whole upbringing and character were too much for her as for them. Perhaps she had thought it fairer and kinder to make it appear that she had done with Giovanni for good and all, and that it was better not to declare a love and friendship that could not be expressed practically. Giovanni, who knew her so much better than I, might have good reason to believe those things. But I had seen her, cold, formal, even cruel, ready to expose Giovanni's friend to the ridicule and insults of her servant. If that was acting, it was not so much superb as overdone.

I sighed, but Giovanni did not notice. He was absorbed in his own thoughts. To my astonishment, he was smiling. The complexities of human nature are beyond unravelment.

But it was useless to speculate too much on the true state of mind either of Lydia or of Giovanni. The danger to the latter not only remained but had been increased by my unsuccessful early-morning excursion. Somehow he had to be moved from my room, and not merely moved, but moved to safety. That was a problem to which, for the moment, I could see no solution; and to have asked Giovanni for his opinion just then would merely have brought trouble on to my head. I felt that for the time being I had had enough.

Chapter Six

ESCAPE TO FREEDOM

We had argued the problem well into the night—that besetting problem of Giovanni's next move; and we were little nearer a solution. Every faint hope was examined and seen to be little more than an illusion. One thing was certain above all: Giovanni could remain in my room for little longer. Every hour almost brought fresh news of Fascist demonstrations, arrests, disappearances, tortures, and murders. The Party was now triumphant everywhere, strong enough to sweep all semblance of opposition ruthlessly aside, and abandon all pretence of allowing freedom of speech or action. And it was showing itself, as dictatorships always do, vengeful and spiteful. Mercy of any kind—other than the mercy the cat shows to the mouse in saving its life as a prelude to torment—was considered a weakness that only decadent and effeminate people could show. Italy had to be virile, ruthless, aggressive, a nation moulded to the emblem of Mussolini's chin.

In such conditions, there was small hope for Giovanni to be forgotten. He had offended the Party; he had even escaped from its clutches. Therefore he was a marked man, and his fate must surely overtake him. It was no good to pretend that, after all, he was an insignificant student who could hardly be expected to rise overnight to the status of a national leader of liberation. The Fascists were set on stamping out even the vaguest and least tangible threat to the utter supremacy they sought to establish—and had, indeed, practically established. Giovanni had revealed himself as a man of courage and ideals; more than that, he had shown himself to be possessed of marked powers of leadership and inspiration, and he had, too, an uncompromising firmness of purpose once he was aroused. Students' riots over a professor in Florence were not likely to cause Mussolini and his advisers in Rome any sleepless nights; but a man with Giovanni's qualities left at liberty was a potential threat, for he might, if unchecked, develop into one of the great enemies of dictatorship—the men who can arouse unquestionable loyalty through appeal to reason and justice and whose power lies in moral strength rather than in brute force.

I was known throughout the University as his close friend; and, as I had pointed out before, if an organized search for him were begun I would almost certainly be among the first to receive an unceremonious call from the Fascisti. But that was not all. Lydia must suspect that I had Giovanni with me, or, at least, must know how and where to get into touch with him. My doubts of Lydia did not lead me to minimize this danger, though I kept them to myself, for Giovanni still retained his faith in her and often relapsed into self-accusations for his thoughtlessness in persuading me to visit her. And there were neighbours. I had one small room in a house in which there were many small rooms. Like the inhabitants of any lodging house, they were a miscellaneous lot, whose sympathies and opinions were as varied as their appearance and occupations. Moreover, sympathies and beliefs counted for less and less. Because the house was cheap, it was chosen by men whose station in life was not exalted and who stood in terror of authority. They might not want to give away a fugitive if they discovered his presence, but the sight of a rubber truncheon or even the peremptory voice of a Blackshirt leader would immediately unloose their tongues.

If the difficulty of getting Giovanni out of the house unobserved was big enough, that of deciding where he might go for safety was even greater. There was nowhere in Italy that offered him safety. The enemy of Fascism was equally its enemy in Turin or Milan or Rome or even far away Sicily. Across the seas there were places that would not hesitate to offer him asylum; but that involved going through a port, and every port was, as the newspapers constantly reminded us, watched with the utmost vigilance to ensure that none of the 'traitors' succeeded in escaping the retribution that stern Fascism had decreed for them. It was a risk he dared not take. There remained France or Switzerland, and the attraction of these lands was increased by the fact that Giovanni spoke French fluently, which would ease his difficulties in a strange country.

Eventually we decided on Switzerland. It may seen fantastic to say that we 'decided' upon it, as though we were would-be tourists selecting our next holiday ground. The difficulty—the stern, challenging problem—remained of how to get Giovanni to Switzerland. The Swiss are a hospitable people, especially to the holiday maker, but they are also strict. They have, throughout their history, rivalled Britain in the asylum they have given to political refugees. Yet Switzerland is a small country with a firm tradition of neutrality and a very understandable desire not to become involved in the interminable quarrels of her larger neighbours. For that reason she does not look kindly on the emigré who attempts to cross the frontier illegally, or on those to whom grave suspicion attaches. No one blames the Swiss for this, but it does create certain difficulties for the genuine refugee, as we soon discovered when, having delineated Switzerland as the goal, we began to discuss ways and means. The problem was not lightened by the fact that Giovanni was a wanted man; there were trials and dangers waiting on either side of the frontier.

'Of course,' said Giovanni, 'I've got a passport, but what's the good of that? In the first place, it's in my room, and I couldn't possibly go back to get it, while if you tried you'd run into trouble for a certainty. The other is that even if I'd got it on me, it'd be useless. The only way I can get out of this country,' he added bitterly, 'is by ceasing to be Giovanni Campo and becoming somebody else.'

The words struck me with the vividness of a revelation. Here was answer to our problem—a simple answer that we ought to have seen at the very start, without all this arguing about it.

'That's the solution!' I exclaimed. 'I've got a passport that'll get you across the frontier; and once you're there, no doubt you'll be able to smooth out all the other difficulties.'

He stared at me as though I had gone stark, raving mad.

'And how do you think that's going to work?' he demanded scornfully. 'Do I look like you? Even a passport photograph wouldn't make your face look like mine.'

'It's the only way,' I returned, refusing to abandon my idea at the first objection. 'The photograph difficulty is easily overcome. You'll have to have that face of yours strapped up for a few more days yet, and that sufficiently disguises you to make any recognition by photo out of the question. As for the description—well, you're about the same height and build.'

He continued to object, but I maintained my position that it was the only possible course. He was probably right in thinking the whole idea crazy and fraught with risk; yet what other course was open? Risk and danger lay everywhere for him; the longer he remained in Italy, the more they increased. Yet, considered in cold blood, the plan had possible consequences that gave me not a few qualms. If Giovanni was caught, he would be utterly doomed. Not only would there be the wrath of the Black-shirts to contend with, but he would be guilty of a serious criminal offence—trying to leave the country by means of a false passport. In those circumstances, little more would be heard of Giovanni Campo. For me, too, there would be dire results. I also should be a criminal; as likely as not I should be expelled from the country as an undesirable alien—or even disappear in company with Giovanni. At any rate, my career at the University of Florence would be ended and the dreams I had of becoming a doctor completely shattered.

'Yes,' I said impatiently, annoyed by my own thoughts, 'of course there are risks. The only question is whether you're ready to take them in the cause of getting to freedom.'

At length he agreed, and we fell to discussing the practical details. If Giovanni was to become me temporarily, then obviously I could not be seen about the streets of Florence; there was no point in adding unnecessary risks to the unavoidable ones. I decided that that very day I should let it be known at the university that I intended to be away for ten days or a fortnight, staying with friends in the country.

'I can do that, as a matter of fact,' I pointed out. 'I've had a standing invitation for some time, and if I do go there it will make all plain sailing. That settles that.'

More serious was the question of money. Neither of us was overburdened with wealth, and there was no one to whom we could appeal for aid. I counted out my reserves. They looked pitiful enough, but they would be just sufficient to buy a ticket to Zürich and provide Giovanni with a few lire to cover expenses en route. It would mean hard going for me for some time to come, but it would be possible to manage somehow.

Giovanni looked at me with a curiously grave air.

'You are a very great friend, George,' he said in a low voice. 'I don't know how I shall ever be able to thank you for all this. You're not only stripping yourself of your money for me but you're putting your head in a noose—and the odds are that that noose will be pulled tight before I ever get near the frontier. I was beginning to despair of human nature, George—you've restored my faith.'

'Fiddlesticks!' I exclaimed. 'No one could do less in the circumstances. Anyway, don't let's talk about it or get sentimental. You stay here, and I'll go and make the arrangements.'

It was curious how, after all those hours of fruitless discussion when everything had seemed black and hopeless, all difficulties seemed to disappear now that our minds were made up. A man with a guilty secret, I had expected to be scrutinized when I went to buy a ticket at the agency; instead, I was met like any other would-be traveller with the utmost courtesy. And why should I not have been? My passport was in order; I was not even an Italian subject whose goings and comings were subject to the whims of the Fascist Government. I admit that, despite all my brave, self-sacrificing words to Giovanni, I watched the booking clerk count my hard-saved lire with a pang of regret; they represented months of hardship from which, now, I should win no reward. And it was not until the clerk had placed the ticket in my hand with a grateful and respectful smile that my heart began again to beat normally. I had to resist the impulse to dash from the shop before he changed his mind and decided to denounce me to the Fascists or the police.

Giovanni, too, gazed at the ticket as though he did not quite believe his eyes. He took it, fingered it as a beggar might fondle a five-pound note thrust into his hands by a quixotic benefactor, and then abruptly turned away to hide, as I believe to this day, his tears.

That night he left me. I did not dare to accompany him to the station. Before he left I decorated his face with dressings that suggested he had recently suffered a major car accident; I do not think anyone would have recognized this much sticking-plastered man as Giovanni Campo. That he still limped a little from the treatment he had to his feet countered any suggestion that the dressings were spurious. I gave him my only spare suit, and he had packed a few things in an old case that bore my initials. For an hour or so before he left I had repeatedly called him 'Signor Sava', until at last he had come to respond naturally to the name. So, as he walked towards the door, I felt that the chances were not so bad after all. At least we had done everything we could to ensure success.

Trying as those few days of his remaining with me had been, it was the next week that was to prove the real nightmare to me. We had arranged that he should return the passport to me by registered post, with a note saying that he had found it somewhere in Florence and was therefore sending it to me with a word of admonition for my carelessness. All that was to satisfy the inquisitive censors of the post if they chose to look inside, and to act as a code indicating his safe arrival in Zürich. It was only afterwards that I realized it was nothing more than an elaborate piece of self-deception—for if it had been opened it would have been very difficult to explain how it came about that the letter was posted in Zürich. In our anxiety to take all precautions we had overlooked that simple, elementary circumstance—but then neither of us was a professional criminal.

So for a week I waited in the greatest anxiety. I expected every moment to receive a visit by the police—or even, which would have been worse, from representatives of the Fascisti. Though I tried to reassure myself, after the second day, that if anything untoward had happened, I should have been questioned, if not arrested, already, but it was not very successful. Not until I again had the passport in my hand and read the carefully worded note was I able to breathe freely again. He was safe! The risks had been justified. Our scheme had succeeded.

Three days afterwards I resumed my normal routine at the university. Life seemed strange there without Giovanni Campo, but the riots had subsided. Now that he was gone there was no rallying centre for the anti-Fascists and they succumbed readily to the overt and covert methods of suppression and coercion applied to them. One could get along well enough if one kept control of one's temper and turned a blind eye to the evils that multiplied every day. Beggars could not be choosers— and as a foreigner I was on sufferance in any event.

Six months later I received a letter. It was written in French and signed 'Jean', but the writer could be no one but Giovanni. He wrote as though he was a friend I had met some time before in Zürich. And when he said that at last he had been successful and managed to pass his entrance examination to the medical school of the university I knew what he meant. He had been accepted in Switzerland.

That was the last I heard of Giovanni Campo for five years—five years in which Italy evolved into the complete totalitarian state and the seeds that were to ripen into the weeds of war were sown.

Chapter Seven

TROPICAL MEDICINE

In 1930, now a qualified doctor, I decided to enlarge my experience by every possible means. Italy did not offer any great prospects, particularly as I was not at all inclined to become an Italian and make myself a member of the Fascist Party. My ambitions turned to other fields, where merit, rather than political soundness, was more the criterion of success. If I was a bad doctor and failed, then that would be my own fault; but if I was a good doctor and had to serve fools who held their positions through their being energetic Party men, there would be nothing but humiliation.

It was with a view to exploring openings as well as gaining fresh knowledge that I decided to attend a course in tropical medicine and hygiene to be held in Zürich. It was not merely that the subject itself rather attracted me, for several times I had played with the idea of working, at least for a time while I was still young, in tropical countries, which I had always longed to see. There was the added inducement that the celebrated Alfred Zücher was to be one of the principal lecturers. There is little need for me to introduce Zücher; he is one of those remarkable men who have achieved fame in several different spheres. His work as a medical missionary in Central Africa had been outstanding and made him an internationally accepted authority on tropical disease and medicine. But he was also eminent as a musician and apart from touring Europe from time to time giving recitals, he was also the author of standard biographical works and studies. Apart from this, the Church recognized him as one of the most successful of its propagandists. Zücher, from whatever angle one viewed it, would be well worth hearing.

When I bought my ticket for Zürich, I was reminded of that other occasion when I had performed a similar task. Memories of Giovanni Campo crossed my mind. How often I had thought of him during these past five years, wondering what had happened to him and where Fate had taken him! Since that one note, I had heard nothing of him. He had disappeared completely from my ken, despite the fact that the Fascists had long since become far too powerful to take any notice of such small fry as he had been, and it might even have been possible for him to return to Italy in perfect safety. Many of those who had fled during those turbulent years of establishment had since come back and integrated themselves into the life of the New State. But I think that, in any event, Giovanni's intellectual honesty would have prevented him from doing anything which so much resembled a change of faith and compromise with evil.

Yes, the conditions were very different now, I thought as I bought my ticket. Then I had watched my last few lire disappearing into the till, and sighed at their going. Now, though I was by no means wealthy, I could contemplate the price of the fare with equanimity. I had no desire to rush from the booking-office lest my sin had been discovered. I was as free as anyone living in Italy could be, and my past demeanours were no longer of any account.

The hall was packed for the first of the Zücher lectures; and indeed he filled it to capacity every time he spoke. And this, as I soon discovered, was as much due to his flaming personality as to his eminence. All too often the world authority has an unimpressive platform manner; he is too wrapped up in his subject to have any separate existence from it. Zücher was definitely a personality. He dominated his audience from the moment he appeared and even before he had opened his mouth to speak. I could imagine him equally as a great actor or politician; he had that power to influence men so that it seemed to them that each of them had been taken personally by the hand and spoken to confidentially. It was not surprising that he was one of the Church's most successful missionaries; he could charge others with all the vitality of his own beliefs.

I listened fascinated to his lectures. Medically, they opened the door to a collection of facts as new and strange as any I had heard. They showed me that the doctor in the tropics had to deal with problems almost fundamentally different from those with which the European practitioner has to deal. But what held me more than all was the sight and sound of this great personality in action. There were moments when he had me on the very brink of deciding to abandon all thoughts of European work and dedicating myself to a life spent among the natives of Africa. It was clear that he loved the native people, understood them, and lived their thoughts. But he was not one of those men who had turned native; he remained, whether in the jungle, on a platform in Switzerland, or in a concert-hall in Berlin or Paris, still inescapably Alfred Zücher. And, interested as I was in psychology, that fact opened up speculations and theories about personality that were even more fascinating than the tropical medical problems he so ably expounded. I wondered if that other great man of Zürich, Jung, had investigated the subject.

But this is the story of Giovanni Campo and not my own reminiscences; though, incidentally, it is a tribute to Zücher that, after all these years, I have only to write his name to find myself again reliving the experience of contact with him and speculating on the mystery of his dominance. And it was through my desire to hear Zücher that I rediscovered Giovanni.

It was, I think, after the second lecture. I am almost sure of it, but it does not really matter. At any rate, it was not the first. Lost in reflection on what I had heard and with the influence of Zücher's presence still on me, I was working my way automatically towards the exit when someone caught hold of my arm. For the moment, I took no notice. In that crowd one expected to be jostled; and if this was rather more than an accidental contact, it was probably no more than someone trying to regain his balance after slipping. But the pressure was increased and I heard a voice—a voice vaguely familiar—breaking through my thoughts.

'George, by all that's wonderful!' it exclaimed.

I looked about me sharply.

'Giovanni!' I cried. 'What on earth are you doing here?'

It was Giovanni. He had barely changed, though his face was, if anything, a little more serious, and, of course, he looked a little older. We shook hands warmly, but it was no place for the talk that bubbles up on an unexpected reunion. People pressed round us, giving us black looks and pressing us on, as we stood temporarily making a block in the stream.

'Come,' I said. 'Let's get out of this place. We'll go and dine, and then you can give me your news.'

He smiled and nodded, and we struggled onwards towards the door. It was curious that I found myself comparing his personality with Zücher's. Giovanni was strong, too, but in a different way. His was the quiet enduring kind of strength that moves mountains by faith, yet is also, as during those student riots, capable of decisive and vigorous action when it is necessary. Zücher, on the other hand, was not so much the mountain-mover as the volcano. He did not persuade, cajole, or reason, but irrupted into one's conscience and mentally bludgeoned one into acceptance, both of him and his ideas. It was a good thing, I decided, that he had elected to use himself for noble ends.

At last we gained the street, and the night air struck pleasantly cool after the hot and crowded atmosphere of the hall. There is nothing so refreshing or exhilarating as emerging from a hot, stuffy room into the pure, clean air of the night.

'Do you live here?' I asked Giovanni suddenly.

He nodded. He was curiously uncommunicative and thoughtful.

'Then show me to a café where we can sit and talk,' I said.

Again he nodded silently. If he could not do better than this, our meeting was not going to be a very great success.

But under the influence of some simple food and a bottle of wine, he came out of his cloud. He was still the same Giovanni, driven on by a dynamic idealism.

'It's good to see you again, George,' he said. 'You bring back lots of memories, some of them good but most of them unpleasant. I have often thought of you in these years, but I didn't write. It might have got you into trouble of some kind or other, and after all the risks you'd taken for me I didn't want to be a fresh source of trouble to you.'

'Let's forget that,' I said. 'Tell me your news. I take it you're qualified now and practising here?'

He nodded slowly. 'Yes, I qualified all right. I got here just at the right time, you see. The big flow of refugees hadn't started and there was quite a lot of latent anti-Fascist feeling—but you know what the Swiss are; they don't like taking sides openly. Traditional neutrality, they call it. Later, when people were coming over the frontier in trainloads at a time, they became much stricter. But they made no difficulties for me at all. I was allowed to enrol in the medical school almost at once—and that letter I sent you was something more than the code we agreed on: it was practically literal truth. And since then, I've been doing all the little jobs of medicine—house physician and the rest. But now I've something bigger in view.' He paused. 'All this is being very egotistical,' he added, apologetically. 'Here am I talking about myself, and I've barely asked you how you're getting on. Tell me.'

'There's nothing much to tell,' I replied. But I gave him a brief account of my career to date.

For a little while after I had finished, he remained silent, playing with a spoon. Then, still keeping his eyes on the tablecloth, he spoke in a very low voice.

'Tell me, George,' he said, 'did you ever see anything more of Lydia?'

I shook my head, though I knew he could not see the movement.

'No,' I answered. 'That is to say, I've never spoken to her again. I've seen her a lot from a distance. She was often at university functions, you know. Her father became one of the big noises of the Party and he was appointed one of the Party delegates on the governing body.'

I stopped abruptly, wondering if I had said too much. I could not know where his reflections about Lydia and her conduct had led him. But he nodded slowly—that deliberate nod of his which was often more eloquent than words.

'I wrote to her once,' he said, almost as though he was talking to himself. 'It was a damn fool thing to do, I suppose, but I had to do something about it. I couldn't stop thinking about her—and I can't even now. Strange how a woman can get hold of a man like that. I never believed it, but it's true, so true, George. Of course, she didn't reply. Everyone who came from Italy I asked about her, and little by little I pieced together much the same as you've just told me. She and her family have become leading Fascisti.'

'I'm afraid so, Giovanni.' I paused and took a deep breath. 'I had that impression when I saw her that day, but I didn't like to tell you.'

And once more he nodded. 'Yes, I know. I could feel that you thought she'd turned on me and let me down. I didn't think so—and still don't. It was just *force majeure*, George. In other circumstances, she would have done anything—anything. I know it.'

I could not answer that.

'You don't believe me, George. I can feel that, too. But surely it's obvious? I don't know how far it had gone at that stage, but at any rate she'd been forced to accept the Fascists and didn't dare offend them. So she couldn't acknowledge me. But there is this, George. The thought's buoyed me up so many times. If she'd really believed in Fascism, she would have betrayed me, wouldn't she? She didn't do it. She couldn't. You see, George, she loved me.'

It is astonishing what illusions a man will retain about the woman he loves, even when she has deserted him, deceived him, and insulted him. There is always the complete excuse for her conduct, however infamous it may have been. Nor does intellect play any part in it. Giovanni was one of the clearest-thinking men I had ever met; he hated falsity in argument or facile beliefs. He was incapable of deception and hated deceit in others. Yet here he was, after all these years, with glaring evidence in front of him, evidence that he had himself laboriously collected, no doubt at considerable pain to himself; and he still believed wholeheartedly in Lydia, was convinced that she loved him. It was an extraordinary state of affairs on which I could find no comment. Luckily he did not expect me to make any, for he went on in the same low voice, as though he was revealing, painfully and reluctantly, his inmost thoughts, his whole soul.

'Often I played with the idea of getting back into Italy by some means or other and going to see her. I would have asked her to come with me and start life in another country—here or anywhere I could make a good living. But I couldn't, George. I believe she would have come— I know it.' He shook his head. 'It wouldn't have been fair. She had had to make one decision that I'd thoughtlessly thrown on her that day, and that was enough. I'm sure she suffered for it, and I had asked already more than any man should ask of a woman.'

I thought of Lydia's cold, emotionless face, of her parting glance of hatred, of her whole manner, on that well-remembered occasion; and I could not share his beliefs. To be frank, I could not imagine that Lydia had the power to suffer on account of others. She was conscious only of herself, and if she loved a man it was because he satisfied some need in her, whether physical or spiritual or material.

His thoughts obsessed him. I think he must have spent many hours of his days going over this ground again and again, using all those great powers of conviction and proof that he possessed to demonstrate to himself that things were as he wished to think of them, prostituting his gifts of logic in the cause of self-deception.

'I'm glad I've met you again, George, and learnt the real truth at last about her situation. You see, I sometimes half believe that the reports I'd got were only half true, but you've shown me what I really knew—that they're the facts. But there's one thing about it that's probably never occurred to you, George—something that's vitally important to me.'

I glanced at him wonderingly. What strange implication had he read into my remarks—which, incidentally, had not gone into detail? I had not told him of how she was a leading figure in the Fascist women's organizations, been one of the guests of honour when Mussolini had visited Florence, or any of her activities as a Party propagandist.

'It's this,' he went on, still toying with the spoon. 'She's rich, George. She's more than ordinarily attractive. She's got family and position—everything that makes her marriageable. Yet she's still not married. That's true, isn't it?'

'No, she's not married, so far as I know,' I replied.

'Exactly. A girl like that doesn't remain single for want of offers. You know that as well as I do. She's faithful to a memory, George. To my memory. It's a great, ennobling thought, yet it is also crushing. It means that I've ruined her life.'

I was speechless. Self-delusion could go no further. If Lydia was not married, that was not due to self-immolation on her part; it was probably due to the fact that she was beating for big game which so far she had not succeeded in putting up. But I knew it would have been useless to argue with him. He depressed me. Here was a man of great talents amounting to brilliance, a man before whom stretched the prospect of a highly successful career, for personality was allied to professional competence in high degree. Yet he was dreaming his life away at the most critical time, living in a world dominated by a false picture of a dream woman who had no contact with reality.

Abruptly he lifted his head.

'You're thinking me a fool, George, I know. But I'm not. Sometimes one feels intuitively truths that logic or experiment can't prove. But I won't bore you any more. I'm sorry I've been so selfish, but it's a relief to talk to a friend. Dine with me tomorrow.'

After making arrangements where and when to meet him, he left me. A feeling of anticlimax descended on me. This reunion should have been a riotous affair during which two erstwhile conspirators relived their successes in defeating their powerful enemies. As it was, it had merely revealed a side of Giovanni's character that was strange to me. Yet, when I came to think it over, it was not so strange. Here again, though in a strangely perverted and misguided form, was that same unswerving determination as had led him to defy the Fascists in all their strength. He had convinced himself honestly that Lydia loved him; and from that position there was no retreat, for reason had established it. I felt a little afraid for Giovanni; determination is an admirable thing, but refusal to admit an error savours strongly of crass pigheadedness.

When I met him the next evening, his manner had changed a little. He was like a man who had at last made a weighty decision which had cost him much in thought and effort. Giovanni was never a gay companion; he was too often sicklied o'er with the pale cast of thought; but that night he was lighter of heart and manner that I could remember him. He smiled when he had ordered a dinner that was, by his standards—for he was a frugal eater—extravagant.

'I hope I didn't depress you last night, George,' he

remarked. 'I'm afraid I allowed my thoughts to master me and became preoccupied. But you see, you were acting as a catalyst to my mental reactions.'

'I'm glad I helped you,' I observed colourlessly, not at all sure what he meant by this.

'I can see you want an explanation,' he went on, 'and in any case I owe it to you after my behaviour last night, so let's get it over and then we can enjoy ourselves properly.'

'Go on,' I urged. 'But don't tell me if it's going to make you feel awkward at all.'

'No,' he returned. 'It's a luxury to have someone to talk to about personal affairs. You see, George, I've been trying to make up my mind about something for a long time, and after what you told me last night I find I'm able to. I can see my way clearly in front of me, and so I know what to do.'

He spoke with the old assurance that he always showed when his mind was made up. I waited attentively for him to continue.

'I listened to Zücher when he was over here last year,' he resumed, after a brief pause. 'Then, he almost persuaded me—not personally, of course, but by his lectures—that working in Africa was just the thing for me. In fact, I practically decided to see him and ask if he had some sort of a vacancy in his mission. But I didn't. All this time, I've held on to the hope that somehow and sometime I should find a way of getting Lydia back to me. I felt I had to remain here, fairly close at hand to her, in case she needed me. After all, one never knew what the Fascisti would get up to. Their friends of one minute are the enemies of the next.'

'Well?' I said dubiously. He was back again on the same track, though his manner was far less introspective than it had been the previous evening.

'I see I've got to get rid of all ideas of that kind,' he continued. 'She's established in the Party, and that being so she'd take her life in her hands if she so much as wrote to me, for I'm quite sure they never take anyone off their black books once they've written his name there. So now there's nothing to stop my going.'

'I see,' I murmured.

'Besides,' he went on with an air not far from outright cheerfulness, 'I think it's my duty to go. While I'm near to her, I'm convinced I'm some sort of a temptation to her. She might try to see me or something like that. If I'm in Africa, the chance doesn't exist.'

He might have been more cheerful. He might have relieved himself of a mental burden. But he was still fundamentally in the same state of self-deception. Lydia probably never gave him a thought, and if anyone mentioned his name would be puzzled.

'And George, you've done such an awful lot for me at various times I hesitate to ask you to do something again, but I must. There's no one else I could ask or trust.' He looked a little embarrassed.

'If I can do it, you know I will,' I said, with no great enthusiasm. A great alarm was surging up within me. I feared that he might ask me to see Lydia again, to brave once more the contempt of her servant and the degradation that she could convey by a glance. But it turned out to be not quite as bad as that.

'If what I think is right—and I know it is,' he resumed, 'it's important that she should know about it.' My heart sank. 'So I'm going to ask you, George, when you get back to send her a note. No need to sign it. It can be anonymous. You need only just tell her that I've gone to Africa. I'll let you know the date of my departure and you can send it as soon afterwards as possible.'

'So you want me to turn anonymous letter writer?' I asked with a touch of sarcasm. I was very fond of Giovanni. I had shown my friendship for him in, I dared to think, a somewhat convincing way. It seemed pushing matters a little too far to expect me now to descend to the writing of anonymous letters. But better that, I reflected, than that he should ask me to see her again—for I knew that when he was in one of his determined moods I would not have had the strength to resist his plea.

He smiled quietly. 'Not in the bad sense,' he returned. 'But it is important—really. You'll do it, won't you?'

'All right,' I answered, nodding, and cursing myself for being a weak fool to allow myself to become tied up with his ridiculous affairs again.

'Thank you, George,' he said, with a happy smile. 'I knew you would.

'And what makes you think you'll be a success in Central Africa?' I asked, to change the subject. I was finding Giovanni rather difficult to understand. There must be some other reason than his desire to 'free Lydia', who, I did not doubt, regarded herself as untrammelled by anyone or anything. Anyone less like the lovelorn maiden eating her heart out for her departed lover would have been extremely difficult to imagine.

'It appeals to me,' he replied, settling himself more comfortably in his chair and gazing reflectively at the deep red wine in his glass. 'I've listened to Zücher a lot, and he impresses me deeply. There's something in what he and his colleagues are doing that calls out to me.'

'In what way?' I asked.

'Lots of ways,' he responded. 'You remember how anxious I was once that there should be a sort of universal health service for Italy, so that everyone could have the same sort of attention. Well I still hold that that's vital, not only for Italy but for every other country in the world. There's a hell of a lot to be done, I know. But I feel now that it's even more important to take medicine to those places in the world where so far it hardly exists. You've got ignorance to fight as well as disease and——'

'There's plenty of ignorance in Italy—and in other countries as well,' I put in rather grimly.

'True—but a different kind of ignorance,' he rejoined. 'In Africa it's a matter of bringing an entirely new system of thought to the people. They're less than our children in some ways. And think of the chances for research.

Zücher's done a lot, but he tells us that for every one problem he and his people have had time to investigate, there are a dozen more on the waiting list and for every one on the waiting list there are a couple of dozen so far barely realized. I remember that description of his—I've used almost his own words. There's more scope, George. Much more scope. Besides, Zücher is a man I'd do anything to work under. I think he's a wonderful inspiration. What do you think of him?'

'He's certainly an outstanding personality,' I replied, 'and that very fact makes him difficult to judge. One's mind is so overshadowed by the man that it's impossible to see his work as clearly and objectively as one should to give a judgment.'

'Oh, his work's marvellous,' said Giovanni. 'You'd better meet him. I've got an appointment with him tomorrow, and I told him I might bring a friend with me. I had you in mind.'

'Thank you, Giovanni,' I observed, taken aback. Giovanni seemed to be reverting to his old role of leader and director of my affairs. But I did not resent it. Zücher would be worth meeting.

'Yes,' I remarked with a smile, 'Zücher's got a wonderfully masterful manner. I wonder what would happen if he found himself up against a riotous mob as poor old Almarini did?'

Giovanni laughed. My remark had the desired effect. He turned away from his personal problems and began to grow reminiscent. Now and again he threatened to return to the Lydia theme but I headed him off with such tactful skill as I could command. It was a pleasant evening, and I left him with lively expectation of the next day's meeting with Zücher.

That meeting proved extremely interesting. At short range, Zücher's personality was almost overpowering. My sensation was something akin to that feeling one experiences in the tropical greenhouse in Kew Gardens. I am sure that he was a powerful hypnotist—but whether his mesmeric powers were automatic or consciously exercised I should not like to venture an opinion.

He professed himself delighted at Giovanni's decision. There was no one, he said—and I think he meant it—whom he would rather take with him as a new recruit to his mission. He did not need ordinary doctors; he needed men whose driving force was idealism and service to God and man and who expressed those qualities in professional brilliance. And at that stage he turned his dark, piercing gaze upon me and said:

'What about you, Dr. Sava? Why don't you consider joining us? Campo has spoken very highly of you to me.'

I shook my head.

'Not yet awhile,' I replied. 'I'm a surgeon, and I've got a long way to go before I can consider myself fully qualified in the way I intend to be. Maybe in another four or five years I might be ripe.'

Zücher laughed. It was a deep, reverberating sound.

'That is well said, Dr. Sava,' he observed. 'Well said indeed. I wish all who call themselves surgeons could hear it and appreciate the implied criticism it contains.'

With that he brought the interview to a close. It had been an interesting experience, not least for the insight it had given me of the relationship between Zücher and Giovanni. For the latter was utterly under the spell of the former. Where Zücher led, Giovanni would follow. No jungle would be too dense, no swamp too pestiferous, to deter Giovanni if Zücher told him to penetrate it; and that would apply, I felt, no less figuratively than literally.

A week later I left Zürich to return to Italy. Giovanni saw me off.

'I shall be leaving in a month's time,' he announced. 'It's pretty short notice, but the Mission help a lot and have most of the gear ready for me, and what I haven't got they'll provide at the other end. That's one advantage of not going out into the blue entirely. I'll let you know when I'm on my way, and I'll write to you regularly. And you won't forget that other matter, will you, George? You'll write that note to Lydia, won't you?'

I repeated my promise as the train pulled out of the station. It had been a strange encounter with a strange ending. And though I was destined to see very little more of Giovanni Campo, from that meeting in Zürich dated a long and imposing friendship that ripened through correspondence and documents so that, in the end, I felt I had known him better than many a man by whose side I had worked all day for years together.

Chapter Eight

NEWS OUT OF AFRICA

Some time passed before I heard again from Giovanni, and I feared that he had forgotten his promise to write to me. But also I hoped. I hoped that he had thought better of his crazy scheme for letting Lydia know that he had left Europe. The idea that I might have to write an anonymous letter that might easily react unfavourably on Giovanni was still distasteful to me.

From curiosity—and also, no doubt, out of a desire to prove my own judgment—I had taken every possible occasion to obtain news about Lydia and to study her from a distance. It was not difficult to see her in public. Her mother was dead and therefore she accompanied her father on all his many public appearances, both at the university and elsewhere. And Signor Buonsanti had become a notable figure indeed. It was generally accepted that, in due course, he would be appointed to even higher posts. Meanwhile he was a leading light of all Fascist undertakings in the city, at which he spoke with a vehemence and vigour that derived little from his own character but a very great deal from conscious imitation of Benito Mussolini.

No doubt it is wrong to judge anyone on the strength of public appearances. The bold, aggressive demagogue, whipping his audiences into mass fervour, is often the meekest of husbands and the most docile of fathers in his own family circle. The woman who presents herself as a leader with anti-masculine tendencies frequently hides within her a burning ambition to be a good wife and mother. Yet something, I maintain, can be gathered on

98

these occasions. A person, man or woman, who basks in the limelight and who is adept at trimming his or her sails to the ever-varying breezes of official policy and public reaction, must have a good deal of the actor and poseur in the character. They are, too, when successful at this game, almost always careerists, ready to sacrifice anything and everything—and anybody—to their ends.

There could be no doubt that Lydia was highly successful in her role of supporter of her father. Her smile was brilliant, her charm overwhelming. Yet one detected underneath a falsity that sprang from calculating coldness. She was inhuman; I had no doubt of it. And a woman to whom that description can be applied was not likely to harbour the ideals with which Giovanni's imagination endowed her. And there were stories about her—stories that were scandalous and in wide currency. One should not believe stories of this kind, however widespread, and I was wrong even to listen to them. But I could not help feeling that though they were grossly exaggerated, there was some substratum of truth in them. Evidence of that was easy to obtain. Let a Fascist notability come to the city, and Lydia was seen everywhere with him on terms, as it appeared, of the greatest intimacy. Frankly, I did not like Lydia. Giovanni's absorption with her was, I believed, a serious breakdown of his normally cool powers of judgment and appraisal.

As the weeks and months went by without word from Giovanni, the unwelcome prospect of writing that note receded until I convinced myself that he had changed his mind. Perhaps the sea voyage had cleared his mind, and distance had enabled him to see the situation in truer perspective. But I was wrong—completely and uncompromisingly wrong. It was six months after I had left Zürich that I had a letter from him—a letter that had come from the interior of Central Africa.

'I expect,' he wrote, 'you wonder what has become of me and perhaps even thought that I have forgotten all about you. But I could never do that, George. No man ever had a better friend than I have in you, and I feel somewhat embarrassed that in my first letter I must ask you to do me yet another favour. You will know to what I refer— the correspondence you promised to attend to for me as soon as I had settled down here. The time has come, my good friend, and I know you will redeem the promise you so willingly gave me.'

I sighed despondently. Here, in the first paragraph, he showed that thousands of miles of travel, a new environment, and, no doubt, curious experiences, had done nothing to alter his extraordinary viewpoint of Lydia. He was a trifle ambiguous in his phrasing, for he feared censors, as all of us in Italy did, but there could be no doubt of his meaning. I was to write to Lydia. The rest of the letter was intrinsically more interesting, but I recall that, at the time, the matter of the note overshadowed it to such an extent that I almost ignored it. I kept it, however, as I kept all Giovanni's correspondence, and some pieces of that first letter I had from him from the ends of the earth are worth quoting.

'As you will gather, I have now moved up country and been attached to the mission. There is little I can say about the journey itself. At no stage was it a pleasure trip, for it seems that even the simplest comforts are regarded as sinful luxuries to medical missionaries. The boat that brought us to Africa was some old hulk that only the strangest fate could have saved, years ago, from the shipbreakers' yard. I will not dwell upon the conditions. Not that I mind particularly. I am no lover of luxury, as you know, but it did seem a little odd to me that men who were travelling to Africa to bring to unenlightened savages the boons of modern knowledge in health and hygiene should be expected to travel under conditions in which the maintenance of both those states was virtually impossible. Well, that part is now far enough in the past to forget, and that is what I propose to do. I will not bore or shock you by a detailed account, the giving of which would, indeed, be painful to me. . . .'

That was not an encouraging start; and from what followed I gathered that already he was beginning to wonder if he had not made a mistake, and if he had not been carried away by a mere passing enthusiasm.

'Here at the station,' he went on, 'things are better than I expected. Our huts are not palaces but they are fairly well built and they are kept beautifully clean. We are in a large clearing in the bush, which is not the most salubrious place on earth. I have not yet had a chance to explore it, and, in fact, I am not yet sufficiently settled down to view the whole thing objectively. My impressions are too many and too strange to make up any sort of coherent picture. In time, that picture will come, and I will try and send it to you.

'What strikes me most are the violent contrasts everywhere. The mere idea of medicine here seems fantastic and absurd. I have been moved back millennia in the human scale, for the local tribesmen are still in an Early Bronze Age level of culture—if you can call it that, for it is nothing like what one associates with similar development in Europe. To read in books of things like sympathetic magic, devils, and walking dead, is fascinating, but it is a very different thing to live among people to whom these things are not merely a reality but a commonplace, to be accepted as naturally as one accepts the beasts of the jungle and the birds of the air. Our medicine is only a particular kind of devil manipulation. One cannot bridge several thousand years of mental progress in a few years.

'Yes,' the letter continued, 'there are violent contrasts everywhere. There is our little operating theatre, which, for its size, is admirably equipped; and less than a mile away there is a native village of hovels where the floors are composed of the dried and compressed ordure of years. Threats, cajoleries, reason, and even drastic measures, are all ineffective to make conditions better. The people cannot see anything wrong in it; it has always been like that; why should they change it? . . .'

And then, after a few more brief details of the place, he wrote about Zücher:

'Above all,' he said, 'I am impressed by the way in which Zücher dominates this place. It is all Zücher. It draws its whole life and purpose from him. I feel that the vast amount of good he has done would all collapse if he chose to leave the place for good. Zücher orders, and the people obey; they look upon him as a most powerful controller of devils and magic. In the mission itself, Zücher is everywhere. His dynamic personality allows of no argument. I have been given six months to attain working knowledge of the local language . . .

'Zücher, too, is responsible for the most curious and fantastic of all the contrasts in which this place abounds. He has a hut like the rest of us, neither worse not better, for he claims no special privileges for himself. There is, however, just one difference. The centre piece of that hut is a concert grand pianoforte. Every night he plays on it, magnificently, as you know he does. And the sound of Bach or Scarlatti drifting out on the night in this place is one of the eeriest sounds in the world. It is the music of another world. At first it pleased me, for it reminded me of happier times in the past, but now I have to confess it terrifies me. I don't know why. When I hear it, I have that feeling which, I imagine, the prisoner experiences in his cell when he sees a patch of sunshine writing its message of freedom on the wall . . .'

The note of regret that ran through this last letter might easily have been due to Giovanni's not yet having been able to come to terms with his new surroundings. Most of us, transported to a new country or new conditions, feel that we shall never adjust ourselves and give way to despondency. But with each succeeding letter—and after that first one they came frequently—the mood intensified and grew at last into active resentment. But the curious thing was that Giovanni had come almost to love the native people and their ways. The difficulty lay in his attitude to Zücher. The bulk of each letter was devoted to the man, analysing him with a superficial air of detachment that concealed a growing irritation.

'Zücher is all-powerful,' he wrote in one letter. 'Sometimes I feel he is too powerful, and that even better results could be secured if we were allowed to use our own initiative and treat the natives less as abysmally ignorant children to be commanded and more as ignorant human beings to be led by kindness into the ways of truth. But maybe my ideas are wrong. I am a newcomer here, and he has the years of experience behind him. I have learnt how easy it is to be deceived by appearances and first impressions in native affairs. . . .'

He deprecated his own views, but the disagreement was growing. I could, knowing Giovanni, sense the increasing tension. He was a firm, determined man when roused, and he did not accept the opinions even of the greatest when he had convinced himself that they were against his own principles. But turning aside from his work, he never mentioned Lydia. At least he had dropped her out of his immediate consciousness. He was immersed in a struggle, and I did not have much doubt how it was going to end. On the one side was Zücher, dynamic and all powerful; on the other was Giovanni, quiet, determined, courageous, a man who stuck to his own opinions. There would not be room for two such people in the narrow environment of a medical mission. In a sense it was the problem of the irresistible force and the immovable object.

The beginning of the end of this brief episode—which nevertheless was to have a determining influence on his future career—came in a letter I received when he had been in Africa almost a year.

'As you know, George,' he wrote, 'I was accepted for this work on a year's probation, at the end of which either side could determine the appointment. I do not know what Zücher thinks of me. Like everyone else I am just one of his people and, as such, probably have no particular personality so long as I do my allotted duties efficiently. But for myself I am in grave and tormenting doubts. I don't know what to do. I have come to feel that my true field is in work like this and not in the civilised places of the world. I don't think I could endure the banalities of European life again for long; but on the other hand, I am conscious of repressions. Sometimes I feel I must resign. At others I think it my duty to remain for another year so as to gain more experience, which would perhaps fit me to undertake some sort of medical mission of my own. There is not much time left for me to make up my mind. I must make my decision—unless it is made for me—within the next month. . . .'

'Unless it is made for me!' Probably he did not realize the prophetic force of those words. For, as it turned out, the decision was made for him, not in the sense that he was dismissed as unsuitable after probation, but because the tacit conflict between his own personality and Zücher's was brought to a head, and on a question on which Giovanni could not compromise. The news came to me in a letter which followed hard on the heels of the one from which I have just quoted.

'I suppose it had to come,' he wrote, 'but I did not expect it to come quite like this. Zücher commands and we obey and so far as the general conduct of the mission goes I, in common with everyone else, accept it. But I am a doctor, George, and I am not going to have my professional opinion called in doubt in the way it has been thought fit to do so. . . .

'I am weary of the restraint that I feel is constantly being put upon me and I should lose my own self-respect if I continued to work while I have this feeling. Only the other day, he told me I was a headstrong lunatic only fit to prescribe for fainting dowagers in drawing-rooms.

'You would, I am sure, have done what I did in the circumstances. I resigned there and then. He was furious, perhaps because I did not give him the chance of dismissing me for incompetence. But there it is, George. I shall be beginning the long trek down to the coast in three weeks' time. Meanwhile I am ostracized, not the first time in my life! I am looked upon almost as a madman, who has had the temerity to question the ruling of a great authority. Well, I have had to fight for my freedom before and I shall go on doing it as long as I live if the need arises. That is the simple fact of the matter.

'Of course, I shall return to Zürich. It is the only sort of home I have. I don't want to come to Italy again, even if it were permitted. What I shall do next, I don't know. But I will get in touch with you when I return and let you know what has happened. One thing I am sure of: my work lies outside Europe. This place, for all the hell it has been to me, has opened my eyes not only to new and strange ways of life, but also to new and strange aspects of myself which I had never seen before. . . .'

So it was ended. The clash of personalities had worked itself out, and in his quiet way Giovanni had again won a moral victory. I put that last letter of his thoughtfully away. He had set out on a curious course that was leading him further and further from the normal walks of man; yet, even then, I felt he was on the right road. Giovanni was a lone wolf, a man who must work by himself in his own way; and amid the ceaseless crosscurrents of Western life he would have been perpetually tossed till at last he might give up the struggle. Right or wrong, that road was to provide for him a strange journey.

PART TWO

Chapter Nine

A NEW HORIZON

No further letters came to me from Africa. For some little while, in fact, Giovanni Campo and his affairs almost slipped from my mind, for it was a period of intense preoccupation with my own affairs for me. Change was in the air, not only in personal matters but over the whole stage of world affairs and the fuses that were to set off the explosion of 1939 were already being primed. If I thought at all of Giovanni, it was in a desultory sort of way. Perhaps I wondered how he was getting on—that and no more. It was almost a shock, therefore, when I received a note from him, telling me he was in Zürich and asking me if I could possibly find the time to see him; he added that he might not be available there for very long.

As matters stood with me, it was highly inconvenient, but I decided that I might as well make the effort. For one thing, I had been working very hard and stood in need of a holiday, even if it was no more than a break of a few days. Apart from that—which was not one of those rationalized excuses for doing something which inclination prompts but necessity denies—I felt it would be interesting to meet Giovanni again and hear from his own lips the story of his African adventures, which I believed, from his letters, he had decided had been a grave mistake and an unwise diversion to his career. Accordingly, I looked up trains and, having made arrangements, telegraphed him to say I would arrive in two days' time.

Giovanni met me at the station. At a glance, it was

obvious he had changed a great deal. He had aged considerably so that now he looked markedly older than his years. Nor was this due entirely to the tropical tan he had acquired, which always makes a man look old; there had been an alteration in his expression. In the past, the determination he had revealed in his anti-Fascist leadership had been largely masked by an expression of shyness and diffidence. All that had gone. I looked at a thin, set mouth, which was yet kindly, narrowed unwavering eyes, and a face that was that of a man who had seen his path in life clearly and was resolved to follow it to the end, no matter where it might eventually lead him. There was nothing startling in the change; all it conveyed was that the essential character was revealing itself more clearly in his lineaments.

He had booked a room for me in the small house in which he was staying, and when we had deposited my luggage there, he took me out to a small café to dine. While he ordered the meal I studied him closely. The change in his manner was more striking than that in his features. He had no hesitation about anything—even the trivial everyday matters of life, to which, hitherto, he had given little attention. But there was, none the less, no suggestion of aggressiveness about him. I felt he would be an unfortunate person with whom to argue or come in conflict but he had not acquired any of the dynamic mannerisms of his erstwhile chief, Zücher.

'I suppose,' he said, when we had disposed of the soup in comparative silence, 'you're wondering what I'm going to do next. Africa is out, George—quite out. There's nothing there for me.'

'If you want me to be frank,' I returned, 'I'm not surprised. It was only a passing phase. You came too much under the influence of Zücher. A pity, really, for it means that you've wasted more than a year up a cul-de-sac.'

His small smile was grim. 'Do you think that?' he asked. 'What do you imagine I ought to do?'

'Get experience—as much as you can,' I replied promptly. 'Develop your great talents as a physician. Take up research. In the end, you'd become an international authority and perhaps win a Nobel Prize.'

He laughed shortly and a little scornfully.

'Very nice. But that isn't my idea at all. My sphere doesn't lie in Europe.'

I stared at him. 'But really, Giovanni!' I exclaimed. A sudden thought dawned on me. 'What is it, then? Are you going to America?'

'That appeals to me even less than Europe,' he answered. 'No. Africa may have been a mistake, as you suggested, but only in the sense that I took the wrong job. No man of my temperament could last long with Zücher. But it proved to me that my instinct was right and that I must work in what you'd call uncivilized surroundings. Zücher is a great man, George—a very great man. His ideals are magnificent—but to me his methods are all wrong.'

'So you're thinking of going on missionary work again?' I asked in stupefaction. It seemed quite incredible.

'More than that,' he replied with an air of quiet conviction. 'I've already made arrangements. I shall be leaving in about a couple of months. That's why I was so anxious to see you. It's even likely that I may never come back again.'

'Where is it this time?'

He raised his head slowly and stared in front of him, like a man who sees a vision.

'China,' he answered.

'But——' I broke out, and checked myself. Impatience surged up in me. It was ridiculous. 'Now look here, Giovanni,' I resumed, rather warmly, 'why have you done this? I should have thought Africa would have shown you the uselessness of it. Listen to me carefully, Giovanni,' I went on, 'you've got it in you to be a really outstanding doctor, to do a great job for medicine, and I'm not trying to be complimentary; I'm only telling the truth. Isn't it your duty to stay where you can put your talents to the greatest use?'

My outburst had made me a little breathless. When I paused, he eyed me with a slight, tantalizing smile.

'I don't agree with everything you say, George,' he remarked casually. 'I don't think I've any special abilities that a hundred-and-one men of my age haven't got, and so they'd be quite as likely to be useful as I am. But I do agree with one thing. You said I ought to be where I can put my talents to the greatest use. That's precisely what I am going to do. I know that such talents as I possess—they're not as many as you think, by the way—can only be used in countries where medical services are poor. I think my duty lies there in bringing my skill, such as it is, to people who stand in real need of it. If I stay in Europe I'm just one doctor among many. If I don't stay, no one will notice my absence, except a few friends, like yourself. And anyway one doctor more or less here doesn't make any difference at all. Out there—well, it's conceivable I might be the only doctor in a hundred or more miles. That's my work, George, and nothing you or anyone can say will shift me from it.'

'I'm sorry, Giovanni,' I apologized; his quiet sincerity and single-mindedness had made me quite ashamed. 'I was only trying to speak as a friend.'

'I know,' he returned, 'and I'm grateful for it. A man doesn't find many friends in this world—I mean real friends, the kind who aren't concerned all the time with how much they can profit by your acquaintance.'

In the silence that followed, I found myself admitting internally that I had been quite wrong and that he was right—as usual. Nor was it entirely his words that had convinced me. I had failed to remember his character, which was now stronger than it had ever been. It had defects as well as high virtues; and one of those defects was his utter belief in himself. Even in the jungles of Africa that isolation of mind and spirit had shown itself in a resentment of direct authority. The only higher power to which he would bow was that of reason. If he was given an order that was obviously and undeniably backed by reason, he would obey, because not to have done so would have been to deny the very thing he worshipped. There are few worldly authorities whose actions are inspired by pure reason and that alone; the element of personality must creep into all of them. Hence it was that Giovanni could only fulfil his destiny if he worked alone or as free from authority as possible. In the civilized countries of Europe, he would find himself continually at odds with some fetish or convention to which lesser men might bow out of necessity, but to which he would never conform because it insulted his intelligence. He was right in his choice, beyond all doubt; and this again was a remarkable indication of his uniqueness. Very few men know themselves so well— especially at his age, for he was then not yet thirty—that they could make a choice of this kind so clearly and with so little hesitation.

I tried to revive the conversation, but though he replied to my questions, I felt that he had withdrawn into himself. Yet I managed to learn a little of what he proposed to do. He was going as a doctor attached to one of the medical units sent to China by a rich philanthropic organization, and though he would have a nominal base much of his time would be spent in moving about the country in a mobile unit.

As he gave details of his future work, he became somewhat more communicative, although he was still a trifle remote as though he were speaking through his thoughts rather than out of them.

'In China,' he said, 'one fights plague and famine and epidemics. I shall be right up against it. I'd rather have that—the feeling that I'm doing a real job all the time— than the knowledge that for every real case I had in Europe I'd have to deal with a dozen or more that have come from pure excess or imagination or stupidity. I could never stand that.'

H   113

There was no comment I could make on this. He was going off into the unknown—an even greater unknown than Africa. Once again he might be deceiving himself, caught up in the glamour of an idea; but for all that I knew he would never change his mind. He had convinced himself that that was where his true field lay, and nothing now would persuade him otherwise. No doubt in his own soul he had worked it all out, putting up all manner of arguments against the proposal—arguments I could not even think of—and rejected them all. That was Giovanni Campo.

'Yes,' he went on reflectively but with that same air of distance, as though he were talking merely for my sake, 'it will be hard work. The biggest difficulty, though, is going to be the language. I'm learning Chinese, but I understand there are many dialects and some of them almost deserve the title of different tongues.'

'So you've started to learn Chinese already?' I asked. It was typical of him.

He nodded. 'Yes. Better than arriving with no knowledge of the language at all. After all, it's when you first arrive in a new country that you want to ask the most questions.'

Once again the silence descended. I could do nothing to break it. My spasmodic efforts to reopen the talk were not actually ignored, but I always felt, even when he gave quite detailed answers to my questions, that he had barely heard the latter. From time to time he gave me a quick, searching glance, as though there was something he wanted to say but hesitated to raise it. As I could not be sure of it, I did not ask him outright what was the matter; if he had, my very perception might put him off completely.

We had finished our dinner, and the silence had lasted so long that I was on the point of proposing we went back to our rooms, when he suddenly leant forward.

'George,' he said in a low, but intense, voice, 'do you ever see anything of Lydia? How is she getting on?'

The question flabbergasted me. If his African experiences had not cured him of his zeal for taking his skill to the ends of the earth, as I had hoped it might, I certainly had believed that it had put Lydia in her proper perspective in his mind. The tone of his voice, however, completely disposed of that idea; it revealed a man to whom this was the most important thing in the world.

I shook my head. 'I hear of her, of course,' I replied, 'but only in a general sort of way, as everyone else does. One can't go much about Florence without hearing something of the Buonsanti family. They're right at the top of the local Fascist clique.'

It was impossible to resist that thrust, though I knew it would probably hurt him. When a man is making a fool of himself over a woman—and especially when that man is a highly intelligent and normally extremely perceptive man—rough tactics are sometimes the only means of bringing him to his senses. None the less I was afraid, even as I spoke, that all attempts of that kind were likely to fail. If he had managed to retain his absorption in her throughout his stay in Africa, far away from even the hint of her presence or influence, it would need something stronger than I could apply to eradicate the virus—for virus I believed this devotion of his to be.

He sighed, a bitter, sad sigh.

'You see, George?' he said. 'That illustrates what I was saying just now. If you stop in Europe you're never your own master. Somehow and somewhere you've got to prostitute all that's best in you. Poor Lydia! How she must hate it all!'

This time I was far too astonished to make any comment whatsoever. From what I had seen and heard of Lydia, she was very far from hating the eminent and limelit position she now occupied, with her father as a Fascist power of the city and almost unlimited power in her hands. And I reflected grimly that, if stories were to be believed, the word of disparagement he had used was, in her case, far more likely to bear the literal, everyday meaning than the figurative one he had intended. I was convinced, as most people were, that the only reason for Lydia's continuing single state was that she had not yet succeeded in enclosing a fish large and golden enough for her taste in her net.

'She's not—married, is she?' he asked, hesitating significantly before that word as though the very thought pained him.

I shook my head. 'Not so far as I know; and if she were I'm sure all Florence would know it,' I added maliciously.

Again he sighed, 'It's a pity. I'd hate to think she was wasting her life and her opportunities over me. How I wish I could see her!'

'I wonder if that would help?' I rejoined. 'She seems to be getting along all right, and perhaps it would be very painful for both of you.'

To my surprise he nodded. 'Yes. It would be, and that's why it's better to leave things as they are. Perhaps after all things are working out for the best. Time will reconcile her to her position, and she may even marry. It's a hard thought, but I suppose it's got to be faced, and I'd hate her to be unhappy because of the thought of me. And out there, in China, I shan't be tempted to do something which might remind her of me.'

For the first time since I had met him I had a sudden suspicion of his judgment. Only half an hour before I had convinced myself that he was going to China for no other reason than that he had proved to himself by rigorous analysis that that course was best for his career. But that remark raised doubts. I still believed that he thought his destiny lay in China, or at any rate in some remote part of the world; but had he arrived at that conclusion solely by logical processes? Rather, were his premises sound? Might it not be that unconsciously he was swayed by this insane desire not to put himself in Lydia's path, as he might if he remained in Europe—that, in effect, he was behaving no more rationally than that stock figure of ridicule, the jilted lover who goes big-game shooting in

Kenya? The ways of the human mind are so erratic and tortuous that it was far from being impossible. But I was not going to raise the question with him—at any rate at that moment.

So, for the final time, the conversation fizzled out once more, and in a little while we left for our rooms. I was remaining three days in Zürich and had looked forward to the visit, but now I was not so sure that my free time might not have been spent better somewhere else in relaxation. For Giovanni, with this obsession upon him, was not going to be a very cheerful or easy companion. I might, if I did not keep a close watch on myself, blunder into some remark that might hurt him or bring down the vials of his wrath on my head; and a feeling of constraint in what one is permitted to say is hardly a happy augury for a holiday. I would have been happier going about my normal routine as a house surgeon.

It was not so bad as I anticipated. Having asked me about Lydia—and I suspect that his desire for news of her was the main, if not the only, reason for his asking me to Zürich—he did not refer to her again until, as I shall relate, the very end of my visit. Meanwhile he became quite cheerful and in better spirits than I had seen him since the Fascist affair cast the first shadow across his life. He could speak now of his coming trip with enthusiasm— and that it was real enthusiasm could not be denied, for his eyes lighted up and he described almost boyishly the ideas he had in mind for experiment and observation. The doctor in Giovanni, the man I had admired in the university, was again uppermost, and for myself I forgot all about Lydia and her influence over him—so much so that once again I found myself regretting that the services of a doctor so full of the promise of brilliant achievement should be lost to the medical schools and laboratories of Europe.

There were five minutes left to go before my train departed and we were standing by the carriage door so that I could jump in and claim my seat the moment there were signs of activity. We had exchanged goodbyes, good wishes, and promises to correspond regularly—promises which unlike most of their kind made on these occasions we not only intended to keep but did, as time proved, redeem handsomely—and suddenly he gripped my arm. There was a dark, brooding look on his face, and my heart sank. The cloud of Lydia had surely settled upon him again.

'George,' he said in a low voice, 'there's one thing I want to ask you. I'm going a long way away and I'm leaving all this behind, but you know that I shall always be thinking of Lydia.' He spoke the name with an almost sacramental tone and he caught his voice in something very like a sob. 'I can't bear to think she should ever be friendless. So promise me this, George—if ever she needs help or is in trouble of any kind, you'll do whatever you can for her. Please, George, for my sake. You've done so much for me I'm sure you won't refuse me that, even though I know you don't think much of her. Oh, and one thing more—if it should ever happen that she needs *me*, George, cable me. I'll come to her whatever the cost. You will, won't you?'

I gave my promise without enthusiasm, though genuinely enough. It was neither the place nor the time to start an argument. Besides, I was never likely to be called upon to redeem the promise. I could not imagine that the successful, wealthy, haughty Lydia would ever stand in need of the help of a poor and recently qualified young doctor painfully trying to struggle along the rocky path of post-graduate study. Indeed, the mere idea of it was so ridiculous that even at that moment which Giovanni obviously regarded as of great solemnity I had to resist the desire to laugh outright—which he would probably have entirely misunderstood.

We said goodbye again, for officials were calling on passengers to take their places. He gave me a last hand-clasp.

'Thanks, George—you're a true friend,' he whispered.

'You won't forget your promise, will you? I know you won't.'

Almost cheerfully I vowed that I would fulfil it if occasion ever arose, at the same time reassuring myself that it never would. And in that events proved me wrong—as they so often have. I was not born to be a seer. If I had been, no doubt I should have applied my second-sight to my own affairs, which had reached a turning point. In the train, in fact, I forgot all about Giovanni and his problems and fell to contemplating my own. This might be the last journey I would ever make into Italy, I reflected. For I had decided to try my luck—temporarily at least—in Germany, then regarded as the fountain-head of surgery; and though the decision had been reached and the preliminary arrangements made, I did not know whether to be glad or sorry. Such is the egotism of Man that Giovanni's perplexities seemed insignificant beside my own.

Chapter Ten

INTRODUCTION TO CHINA

I have never been to China, and anything I write in these pages of that vast and baffling land can be no more than impressions gathered through another man's eyes. Wherever possible I shall use Giovanni's own words, but in any case the views that are expressed will be his and not mine. And here, of course, there is the danger that, when I report at secondhand, so to speak, an element of misunderstanding or false stress may creep in further to distort the picture. It is necessary to point this out lest someone who knows China intimately reads these pages and rises up in righteous wrath at inaccuracies of fact. Let him remain in peace. For my purpose, it is no handicap to be no student of China and its mysterious affairs, for I am writing not of China but of Giovanni Campo, doctor and friend. I shall try to present China, whenever it is necessary to do so, as he saw it—which was, after all, no more than one man's glimpse of it. But for the rest I am concerned to make my portrait of Giovanni as complete and faithful as my knowledge of him, which is neither superficial nor sketchy, permits; and if the portrait be good it does not matter overmuch against what background it is set.

In those early days of his work in China, Giovanni wrote to me freely and often. He was going through the difficult period of acclimatization and he needed a confidant, someone to whom he could convey his reactions to a culture and scenes that were fundamentally different from all in his experience. To Giovanni the need of such a confidant would be very great. He had none of the mentality of the tourist or the sightseer which would have enabled him to ask stupid questions; he preferred to learn by experience and observation, and I think that his life in Africa, while it had removed some of his outward diffidence, had also deepened his self-containment, which amounted at times to isolation.

His earliest letters were probably no different from those which come from every observant man who goes to China, for they tell of a great and growing confusion of impressions, some of them so contradictory as almost to baffle the reason. Life in China was not merely strange; it was fantastic and incredible; and he found the Europeans little help to him in sorting out his fantasies. 'I find the majority of these Europeans almost as unbelievable as the country in which they have settled,' he wrote. 'They live almost apart from the country and most of them have contrived to delude themselves into the belief that, in some mysterious way, China does not exist for them. They go to their clubs and dine in the Western way; they drink Western drinks; they think their own thoughts. For them, whenever they allow themselves to think of it, China is either a source of profit and to be endured for that reason, or else a sort of superior prison to which they have been condemned. Needless to say, it is the business men—the bankers, the merchants, all the Socialist propagandists call the "exploiters"—who belong to the first class, and the consuls and other European government officials who belong to the latter.

'But I have already learnt one thing that is perhaps worth recording,' he went on. 'It is why the British are so successful in colonization. To us, in Italy, the British seem self-contained and aloof to the point of rudeness; their preference for their own language and customs—and even, strangest patriotism of all, their own cooking!—seems almost a mania. But out here, among the Chinese, they reveal another side to their character—or perhaps their genius. It is true that they remain insular and pigheaded, clearly regarding themselves as a race apart. The French and Americans, of both of whom there are many, are more friendly and seem more intimate with the Chinese. But it is the British who, when their guard is lowered, come nearest to the spirit of the country and love it most. I was speaking to a man in the club soon after I arrived in Shanghai—a typical Englishman whom one could imagine in tweeds and carrying golf clubs or a sporting gun, and whose main interests in life appeared to be the whisky bottle and the London *Times*. Yet it was he—and he only —who could address the Chinese boys fluently in their own language. And it turned out that he was by way of being an authority on Chinese literature and had even written poems in Chinese that had been highly praised by native scholars for their formal perfection and also for their intimate reflection of Chinese thought.

'A little later, I plucked up my courage to ask one of these perplexing Englishmen how it was that not only, as I had learnt, had he been in various consular and similar posts in the country for over twenty years but also he had never returned to England for his leaves; he had gone to Japan, Malaya, India, Australia—anywhere but home. He looked at me and smiled in that rather superior English way—we talked in French, by the way, in which he was quite fluent though his accent was execrable—and said: "England is an illusion, a mere idea. To you, Italy is the land to which you want to return because it is your home. You think of its comforts, its climate, its scenery, its associations. But to me, England is a dream. It is a home that never existed, because the reality is nothing like the vision, and we know it to be that, whereas you delude yourself into believing that the vision and reality of home are one and the same thing. I shall go to England when I retire, and I shall be a stranger. I shall have no home because no Englishman has a home unless he has 'settled down', a process that takes years. I shall be a bachelor, and therefore to be pitied, and I shall be at the mercy of housekeepers and landladies, one of whom perhaps I shall eventually marry. I shall find it cold and draughty. My pension will hardly be sufficient for me to live upon in decent comfort. Here I can regard the Chinese and fellow white people like yourself with tolerant superiority, because, as an Englishman, I am expected to do that; but in England I shall be one of millions of other equally depressing people. . . ."

'I have not met many English people in my life, though plenty of tourists came to Zürich while I lived there. I am too easygoing and trusting to regard them as typical of the country that has dominated the world for so long. But I believe they have a very peculiar sense of humour, and perhaps this gentleman made me a victim of it. I do not know. But this, too, I have learnt—that out here, when all white men are thrown into high relief against an utterly alien background, one sees more affinity between the English and the French, say, than between the English and the Americans, despite their common language. It is a remarkable discovery. . . .'

Some of Giovanni's letters were many pages long—and I regret to say recorded nothing more original than is to be found in the pages of the most pedestrian of travel books of the *My Three Months in China* type. He thought nothing too trivial to be remarked upon. But, little by little, his impressions grew clearer. The vast confusing scene resolved itself into coherent groups and patterns, which made some sort of sense within themselves however incongruous they were to each other.

'Now I am beginning to get my bearings,' he wrote, 'I am seeing many things that were hidden from me before. My sense of strangeness here is quite different from that I felt on arriving in Africa. There I had stepped back several thousand years in man's history; I could not help feeling that I belonged to a superior culture, even to a superior and more accomplished species of Man. But in China one cannot have any feelings of that kind. It is true that much of what one sees, hears, and learns, strikes one as primitive and obscure; yet also one has the feeling that it is oneself who is the intruder, and that trying to infuse one's own knowledge (far less to impose it) is an impropriety, almost an insult. Here is a true culture, with its own learning, its own philosophy, from which the West has learnt and will continue to learn. It has been thus for—how long? The usual statement is two thousand years; at any rate for longer than most nations of Europe have existed. So one's impression is not that of being the carrier of a lighted torch, but rather that of being a competitor, and sometimes a rather vulgar competitor at that. I am still very green, of course, and perhaps one day I shall modify that view. . . .'

Yet he continued to find contrasts that staggered him and a mode of thought that baffled him completely, as it does most Europeans, if not all.

'Today,' he said in another letter, 'our busy writers and reporters are always talking of "Modern" China or the "New China", as though the innumerable revolutions and rebellions had upset the whole mode of life of the country. Yet I am prepared to believe that if one of the ancient Chinese could come back, he would find very little unfamiliar in his country. He would rage at the presence of so many foreign dogs, or devils. He would detest the growth of commercialism on the Western model and would find some of the customs of the Westernized Chinese utterly repugnant. But when he moved away from the great Westernized cities of the coasts and rivers, he would return to the land he knew. Here, time has stood still in all essential features. The hand of the past lies heavy everywhere upon the people and their thought. And that is why, I think, the Chinese have gained the reputation, not wholly deserved, so far as I can see, of being a contemplative race. Their lives are so ruled and ordered by established customs and conventions, even to the turn of their conversations, that they have gained a serenity and lack of dynamism that is unbelievable to Western minds, which accordingly credit the Chinese with powers of the deepest reflection.'

It was when, at last, after exhausting and often hopeless travel by river and overland, he arrived at his station that he began to get nearer to the people among whom he had chosen to work. And at once it seemed he came face to face with the fundamental difficulties confronting the medical worker in China.

'I have got to the stage,' he observed in a later letter, 'when the first thing I expect of a new phase of Chinese life is a violent contradiction. This applies not only internally, so to speak, by which I mean as regards China and Chinese themselves, but particularly in relation to Western ideas. I am beginning to believe that their very method of thought, the actual working of their brains, is different from ours. It would be fascinating if a team of psychologists could investigate that point, though it might, of course, have disastrous results on what we call the science of psychology by invalidating its claim to provide a universal explanation of mental processes. At times I am ready to discover that, to a Chinese, two and two do not necessarily make four. . . . But this is getting away from the point I was trying to make about contradictions. I have already, after a fortnight engaged in settling in and a further fortnight in actual practice at the clinic here, come to the conclusion that the Chinese are incapable of understanding the object of true medicine.

'First of all, there is their attitude towards death. It is, of course, bound up with their ancestor worship and their belief in spirits of various kinds, too involved yet for me to begin to understand. But whereas we think life should be saved at all costs, they hold no such views. A man sees no particular tragedy in dying; he even has his coffin and funeral preparations made under his own direction. After all, he will eventually become an honoured ancestor to whose spirit respect will be paid. Their dead do not disappear, as ours are supposed to do, to some unspecified abode. On the contrary, they remain precisely in their accustomed walks of life, and I have seen bodies in coffins actually retained in the living rooms of their often pestilential huts. It is better to be a spirit with its special privileges than a sick man—a point of view that does not encourage medical treatment.

'Of course, the official view is that Western medicine should be encouraged. That is why we are working here, not only actually practising but training, as best we can, Chinese students. But when one gets into the field one finds a rather different point of view. The military governors, who are the bosses of the towns and cities, and wield almost absolute power till someone else, by chicanery and force, chooses to displace them, welcome us. They comment on the marvels of Western medicine, its powers of healing, and the like—and mean it sincerely, so far as any Chinese, high or low, is capable of sincerity. At the same time they are inclined to ask, in effect: Why all this trouble?

'This will show you what I mean. Almost in my first week here there was an outbreak of cholera in one of the outlying villages. To me, this was alarming enough, as you can understand, but, as you know, this sort of thing is quite common in China, so perhaps it was not surprising that even my colleagues did not seem unduly perturbed. I suppose I made a fool of myself by talking too much about what should be done and the potential danger to life and so on. I expect I am still young enough to talk like a text-book sometimes!

'At last the Chief—he is a German, a fine fellow, but a little weary and cynical after ten years out here—thought he'd teach me a lesson. He told me it wasn't his job to try to clean up the sanitation of a Chinese village (I hadn't seen a real Chinese village then so I didn't grasp the beauty of his understatement) and he wasn't even in a position to undertake strictly medical measures without consent. All he could do was to lay suggestions before the Governor. He had decided, he told me, to send me along, as I was fresh from Europe and had the latest knowledge at my fingertips, to make recommendations.

'The appointment was made, and I went along to talk

to the Governor, who told me, in the usual way, how wonderful Western medical knowledge was and how much it meant to China, where ignorance still unfortunately abounded. This looked encouraging, so I set out at once to tell him what should be done, and how, if he allowed what I proposed, he would win eternal gratitude by being the saviour of thousands of lives, not only directly but also by stopping the spread of the epidemic.

'He listened most attentively to all I had to say and even put some questions to me that showed he had a very shrewd mind and certainly could not be accused of ignorance of Western science. (I found out later he had graduated at Yale in the United States and afterwards spent a year as a post-graduate student in London, at the School of Economics there, I think.) So when he bowed and smiled at me, complimenting me not only on my knowledge but also on my fluency in the Chinese language, I felt that my point was won.

'Not a bit of it. He told me I had convinced him that an energetic campaign would undoubtedly save many lives and keep the outbreak under close control. He was surprised to learn, he went on, that so much progress had recently been made in cholera-treatment. But for those very reasons, he concluded, he was unable to give us the freedom of action for which we asked.

'I stared at him quite dumbfounded. Nothing so utterly illogical had ever come out of a human being's mouth—that was what I felt. Then seeing my astonishment he went on to explain. He told me the province was already grossly and tragically over-populated and that the birthrate was continuing to rise at an alarming rate. The shadow of coming famine already hung ominously not only over that province but also over the neighbouring ones which might, in other circumstances, have helped to supply food in case of need. This plague would undoubtedly seize a good many of those whose unfitness made them burdens on the community besides providing them with the profound joy of becoming one with their illustrious and departed ancestors.

He would give us every facility to treat the sick as far as we were able, but without taking extraordinary measures, such as increasing the staff of the station, and even to check, if we were able, the spread of the plague to the capital. Beyond that it would be a crime against his people to prevent the epidemic taking its course. When I humbly suggested that perhaps his people might take a different view if they knew the truth of what we might achieve if given a free hand, he made a beautifully eloquent gesture, telling me that to the ordinary people these epidemics and plagues were common incidents of life, no more to be fought against than tempests, floods, or famines, to all of which they were equally and fatalistically inured.

'I rushed back to the Chief almost beside myself with indignation, railing against this criminal obstructiveness and callousness of mind. The Chief listened to me and then stopped me quite kindly but firmly. "You've got to learn a lot of things yet, Campo," he said to me. "The Chinese have quite a different set of problems to face and you must learn to forget to apply European standards to them. Morals, after all, are only a statement of practices that are conducive to the welfare of a people, and to apply Western moral concepts about life and so on out here would be to turn everything upside down. You go to bed and think it over."

'It took me quite a lot of thought to see the Chief's point of view, which at first I had put down to his having become, during all the time he has been out here, inoculated with Chinese modes of thought. But in the end I had to admit that he—and the Governor—had a certain amount of reason on their side. Of course, it was a shock to me to learn that, in a country which has produced some of the world's finest art and deepest philosophy, the crude natural forces of disease and famine should be allowed to operate as they do in the jungle to obtain an optimum population, but there is nothing inherently wrong in natural forces. It is only our long-established Western

128

way of thinking that has given them an artificial ethical
value—or lack of it.

'We get so used, in Western medicine, to conceiving our
duty as the saving of life at any cost that we inevitably
overlook the fact that in other lands, still blessed or cursed
with a rising birthrate on top of an excessive population,
it may actually be a crime against society to preserve
life unnecessarily. You may think by now that I am
already coming under the influence of China myself and
abandoning the things that seem to stand at the root of
civilization in general and our profession in particular. I
would not say that—yet; but the fact remains that this
is a land so utterly different from everything we know in
the West that it is really not surprising to find some of our
most cherished beliefs stand on their heads. . . .'

At first sight, it was certainly a very surprising *volte face*
for Giovanni to defend, however abstractly, a policy that
prevented him from using all his skill to save a life or lives;
and I could not help wondering when I read the letter
what would have happened if Zücher had issued such an
edict as the governor had. The answer to that, of course,
was that Africa was not China, and their problems were
far apart. When I reflected on the matter, however, I
came to the conclusion that Giovanni's acceptance of the
principle should not have been unexpected. The governor's
argument was based on sound logic, even if the method
and the result were not particularly attractive; and
Giovanni was powerless in the face of such logic. So I was
not at all shocked or even temporarily surprised when, in
his very next letter, he wrote these words:

'Those Europeans who, like the men in the big coast
cities, cling together in colonies of their own kind and try
to carry on all the traditions of their homelands will
never get to terms with China. China is strange and
curious only because it is utterly antithetic to everything
we take for granted in our own civilization without apply-
ing any sort of examination to it. The one way, as I see it,
to accept this country and be accepted by it is to start

again at the beginning and be ready to reassess every single item of one's beliefs and ideals. In many ways, the Chinese way of life is far more logical than ours, but it wouldn't do to accept all their ways as right on that account, for all too often their premises are demonstrably false. All the same, it goes a long way towards understanding if one can get to realize that one carries about with oneself a good deal that is nothing more than primitive taboo and superstition, useful in our own society but completely unsuitable in many others. A year in China, in that frame of mind—perfect and rational receptivity—would, I feel sure, do every European a great deal of good and enable us all to see that so many of our actions, so grand-seeming to us, are really childish, irrational, and frankly ridiculous. . . .'

Chapter Eleven

ADVENTURES AND GOOD FORTUNE

As the months passed, Giovanni became less concerned with his subjective reactions to the Chinese
scene and the proffering of explanations for what
he saw and heard and experienced than with actual oc-
currences in a strange land ever-ready with some fresh
surprise; and I must confess that these form some of the
most interesting in the whole of the long sequence he sent
me. He learnt to take China more or less for granted.
This happens to all of us. In our first contact with a new
environment, especially one utterly different from any we
have previously known, we look for explanations and
descriptions which not even those long familiar with the
place can give us; we feel, perhaps, that our new and
unbiased vision will discover the truth that has eluded all
those who have preceded us. But in the end we are
absorbed into the life around us, barely aware of its oddity.

These letters, in fact—those covering the latter part of
his first year in China—are amongst the most objective
he sent me. One has to infer his progress and his establishment of terms with his new life, for he rarely mentions
such things directly. An odd hint here and there, a statement of something which he assumes we know but he has
not mentioned before—these and other asides are the
pointers to a progress in his work that must have been
rapid and substantial. There is a change of tone in his
references to individuals. The director of the medical
station, Dr. Hans Messig, is at first mentioned respectfully
as 'the Chief'; after six months, and with no intervening

description of the progress of their relationship, he becomes 'Hans', and there obviously exists a close intimacy between them in which there is a deep mutual trust. In the first days, he always has a colleague or more with him during his medical work; yet as soon as four months after his arrival, he is working alone in remote places away from the central clinic, and he takes it for granted that I know what has happened to him.

This period is, in fact, one of the most remarkable and successful in the whole of Giovanni's career. For a time—almost the only time—he became extraverted and no longer complicated his existence by bouts of acute self-analysis and introspection. If this phase could have lasted, Giovanni might have fulfilled his clear destiny—to become an outstanding figure in medicine. But in the end, as we shall see, that fatal capacity for logic (or pseudo-logic) as a ruling factor in his life returned with full force to be a handicap and a guide into strange paths. I say this deliberately, for it is my contention that no man who strives to rule his life by pure reason can gain true success in a world in which so much is illogical and irrational, and in which emotion is a considerable, if not, indeed, a controlling force. This is true, I believe, even of occupations like science and medicine in which cold, detached judgment seems to be paramount.

The China in which Giovanni was working, in the years immediately preceding the Japanese intervention in Manchuria, was, as he pointed out repeatedly, a strange place:

'Here are old and new, East and West, Chinese and European, side by side, mixing but never forming a true amalgam or combination even among the people themselves,' he wrote, quite early, but after the first strangeness had evaporated and he was more at ease with life. 'One meets in the ports and commercial centres Chinese who, apart from their racial features, seem to be European. All of them speak English—though one Englishman told me that it was not English but American; I am no judge of that. They wear the same sort of clothes as the European colony. They have been to European or American universities and they talk in the manner of educated Europeans. This, one thinks, is the New China; the West has conquered by peaceful penetration where through millennia no one else has. But it is only a gloss on the surface. Those same men, removed to administrative positions in the interior, revert at once to type. They forget their Westernism and become the old-time Chinese governor or official, living by graft and oppression—which is perhaps made worse by the greater subtlety in these things they have learnt from their Western masters. They admit torture as part of the normal machinery of government; they accept such things as plagues, epidemics, and famine, as the ordinary course of natural events. Like the humblest coolie, they live only for today, for it is implicit in the whole Chinese philosophy that tomorrow can be only a repetition of yesterday and is therefore barely worth consideration. Time stands still in that sense: it is always the same day, the same hour. . . .'

He went with his mobile unit to some village many miles from his base. It was not an emergency summons but one of the routine mission calls of the medical organization. The visit was overdue, for there had been trouble in the area—there was and is always trouble in China—and it was considered dangerous for foreigners to go there. But the war between the local powers had been finished more or less amicably. The erstwhile bandit general had supplanted the local governor and become the official representative of social order and law; the ex-governor had retired to his estates in the country taking with him, as was usual in these cases, all the available liquid assets of the province he had ruled; and there had been the usual exchange of courtesies between either side. It was a normal incident of Chinese life to which no one paid any particular attention. The revolution made little difference to the merchants, shopkeepers, or soldiers. The former would have to foot the bill, while the latter stood no better chance of being paid regularly by their new commander than by the old.

'It was described as a revolution,' said Giovanni, writing to me about the affair, 'but no one would have thought that the town had suffered any change at all. It was just the same as the other places I had been to. The trading classes groaned under the extortion to which they were submitted; the military and police looted whenever they could. In fact, life was as it had always been, and one thinks sometimes it will always be, in China. We were welcomed with the elaborate courtesy and compliments to which we have become inured, and with the same indifference to the reality of our work as we encounter everywhere. They flatter us by thinking we can cure anything and everything—and insist that if we confess a case hopeless it is only because the bribes offered us have not been sufficient to induce us to use our most effective remedies.

'One woman came to me with a septic finger. It wasn't really bad but it had to be opened up, and I sent her away with a rather impressive dressing on the wound. Next day half the women in the streets appeared with dressings on their fingers. On inquiry I learnt that such dressings were obviously powerful charms against the evil spirits who cause pain and swellings in the finger—poisoned wounds are quite common here, which is hardly surprising amid all this filth—and it is better to be sure now than sorry afterwards even if the "charm" makes manual work a little difficult. We are not bringing new and scientific medicine to them but only more powerful charms, and our most beautiful treatments are different in degree but not in kind from the evil ointments of putrid dung that the local doctors prepare. . . .'

This was only an incident, vividly though it lights up one phase of Giovanni's daily life. The trip was memorable for him for quite other reasons, only indirectly medical.

'I never thought,' he wrote in his next letter, 'that I should become a *casus belli*, but then anything can happen in China, which is one more reason for not trying to plan ahead or take thought for the morrow. But it has happened. Our new Governor, one Seng, the ex-bandit, has run into trouble much sooner than he had any right to expect, for he certainly has not had time to recoup himself for the expenses of the campaign which brought him to power. The retired Governor has not kept to the rules; he —General Fung—has staged a counter-revolution after an indecently short interval and by original means. He promised the soldiers the back pay he owed them—they all do that—but he surprised everyone by redeeming his promise immediately to those who took him at his word. Needless to say a large proportion of the forces have transferred their allegiance back to the hitherto despised Fung. And this is where I come in. I do not think actual hostilities would have broken out if I had not been on the spot, for the opposing armies were too evenly matched. What usually happens is that the would-be governor waits until he has induced the larger part of the soldiery of the established governor to desert to him. At that point, the established governor gracefully retires and his opponent takes over. It is practically bloodless.

'What happened was this. Fung was taken suddenly ill and sent a messenger to me asking me to attend to him. The details were harrowing. Fung, it appeared, was at death's door. Without hesitation I set out with a couple of porters. As I had Fung's own messenger with me I did not think it necessary to provide myself with an escort against possible attack.

'Attack came—but not from the soldiers of General Fung. On the contrary I was pursued by a detachment of General Seng's army, who caught up with me almost within sight of my destination. The commander pointed out with the utmost politeness that Fung was a rebel and a bandit and the governor could not possibly allow me to provide my services for him. For such an outlaw death with the direst pains would be too merciful an end. There was nothing to do but bow to superior force and prepare to return. It was just on nightfall and the journey took a day at least, so we encamped for the night. I will not harrow you with details of what a Chinese bivouac is like. All that can be said of it is that it is one degree less nauseous than a regular encampment, for it does not contain the accumulated filth of months or weeks.

'One point had been overlooked. We were in Fung's territory. Not only that but Fung's messenger had managed to escape. In the morning, Fung's men attacked with superior force and overwhelmed Seng's detachment. Once again I was on the road to Fung's headquarters. I duly arrived there only to find the sublime general with an acute attack of indigestion that he could easily have treated himself with a few bismuth tablets—but that is by the way. The assault on Seng's soldiers roused the reigning governor to fury and he forthwith dispatched a powerful force to haul me back. News of its advance reached me as I was on the point of setting out on my return journey. Forthwith I was placed under arrest by Fung; he could not now allow me to fall into his rival's hands.

'Now I refuse to be held prisoner by a bandit general. The camp was in confusion, for it was against all the rules for the governor to attack it, and so it was easy for me to make my escape. I did not know where I was going; the important thing was to go. But now, it seems, I had acquired a special status. If Fung let me go, he would lose face. Similarly if Seng permitted Fung to capture me, he, likewise, would lose face. I had plotted out a route that took me through the mountains whence I could rejoin the road that would take me back to base, and I thought I had succeeded, for I counted on the two armies being so concerned with their own affairs that they would ignore me. I was quite wrong.

'On the second morning, one of my porters pointed out a small column of men climbing up the southern slope towards my overnight camp, and it soon became clear that they belonged to the Fung army. Almost simultaneously, another posse was spotted approaching from the western slope—and these proved to be Seng's soldiers. I promptly struck camp and made off down the northern slope, which in any event was my proposed route. I thought I might as well leave the two parties to fight it out between themselves.

'This is perhaps the strangest thing of all. They did not want to fight it out. All they wanted was to capture me. After an excited parley, they set off in joint pursuit, apparently on the most amicable terms, and it developed into a race in which I was the prize. The prospect was not very encouraging, for I felt that once one side or the other had captured me, the unsuccessful one would again grow warlike and seek to seize me by force. But—since this is China—the incredible happened: both sides reached me at once, and I found myself seized on either hand by the respective commanding officers.

'Luckily I have been in China long enough—and have not had to waste too much time in learning the language— to realize the value of stratagems, and forthwith I began to talk. I pointed out that as an unworthy foreign devil I could not aspire to be of any importance in their honourable internal affairs and that I was but a doctor seeking to do my duty. I did not claim the honourable status of a soldier and so could not be a prisoner of war. I said that I obeyed the sublime General Fung's summons to treat him because it was my duty to do so; and now equally it was my duty to hasten to the no less sublime General Seng, in whose honourable features my experienced eyes had detected signs of a coming malaise. (I had not; but that does not matter; it is the sort of lie that is quite normal in China, where truth, as an absolute, is unknown.)

'The two officers bowed to me and I think they bestowed on me a look of admiration, for I had proposed to them a formula that would save face on both sides and leave me free to return to the rest of my unit, the detention of which might easily lead to international complications of a kind they wished to avoid. The rather tame ending was that I was allowed to proceed on my way—but, so as not to offend the susceptibilities of Fung's men, I went alone with my porters and not with the escort thoughtfully sent for me by Seng.

'So there you see is how I became a *casus belli*, performing the seeming miracle of spurring a Chinese general unblessed with overwhelmingly superior forces into active measures—an achievement of which I suppose I have some right to be proud.

'But this long story, which has probably tired you, had a sequel almost as surprising. My story of General Seng's coming indisposition had been a pure invention. But the General, convinced now that his chances of maintaining himself in his proud office were infinitesimal—for even the escort he had sent for me had eventually decided to return to Fung's camp instead—insisted that he was a sick and ailing man and that the distinguished and erudite Western doctor had told him he needed a protracted rest in the peace of his estates! Even in China, it seems, "medical reasons" provide a graceful cloak for official resignations. . . .'

An incredible adventure indeed! Yet its very absurdity is the Chinese hallmark of authenticity.

Not long afterwards I received a somewhat short and depressed note from Giovanni. He had been recalled to the central clinic. Despite his reserve (or perhaps because of it) and his intellectual sureness of himself, he was extremely sensitive to words or actions that carried the faintest hint of criticism of his efficiency, and that he believed this recall to be due to something of the sort was evident, though he did not mention it openly. I feared the worst. Giovanni, smarting under implied criticism of his behaviour, might readily throw in his hand, and then, once again, his talents would have to seek another outlet.

His forebodings were, however, very far from realization. On the contrary, that summons had quite a different purpose from criticism or blame and his next letter, addressed from the central clinic, had an air of stunned surprise about it, such as a man shows when something quite unexpected, and even undeserved, has befallen him. Giovanni's luck was in the ascendant.

'When I started off for the central clinic,' he said, 'I did so gloomily, as perhaps you guessed from my letter. I scented Trouble with a very big "T", and I wondered if my intrusion into the maze of Chinese politics by way of the two generals had counted against me. That certainly had nothing to do with it—the story merely provided the mess with a good laugh.

'No; what has happened is something I can barely believe even now. It seems too good to be true. Hans Messig, our Chief, sent for me as soon as I had rested after my journey, and when I went into his office I found another man with him whom he introduced as Daniel Hickford. That made things look even more serious—for this American is the Director and President of the whole organization. My heart sank. Surely I had broken all sorts of rules if the President wanted to see me. But he chatted quite pleasantly, and in the end he told me that a new station was being started up in Jehol, near the Manchurian border, and that he had talked things over with Hans, who had—hold your breath!—recommended me to take charge of it! I was too astounded even to be able to thank him for a whole minute at least. And I had expected a dressing down!

'This is wonderful news, George, isn't it? I have been out here little more than fourteen months now, and here am I what they call a Chief of Station and Clinic Director, when there are men who have been out here much longer than I and with far more experience. I can't repeat all the nice things Hans said about me; he even brought in the Fung and Seng affair and said it showed how far I had penetrated into the Chinese mentality, when it was no more than a lucky stroke of inspiration. But there it is. I shall be starting off soon to the new location. A small staff will be sent to me from the recruiting places the organization has all over the world, for we are absolutely international.

'You can hardly imagine how much this means to me. I shall be my own, unfettered master. In between whiles I've been thinking a lot and I've already got quite a few ideas I should like to try out in actual practice. This will be my great chance to do so. Provided we don't get into trouble with authority or authorities, for there are dozens in China—and one doesn't overspend too violently on one's financial allocation, one has an absolutely free hand. I shall be very rushed making preparations—it has all come so suddenly—so I may not write again for some time, and when I do it may be as a fully fledged Chief! My luckiest day was when I decided to make my life's work in China. . . .'

People sometimes call me a pessimist because I believe—experience has forced me to—that it is when Fortune smiles most sweetly that one has to be most keenly on one's guard. So it has always been with me. I rejoiced at the good luck, far from undeserved, which had befallen Giovanni. He was a born leader with an original mind that could not long remain in subservience to anyone else, and some position such as this was ideal for him. But also I had an uneasy feeling that his luck was too good to be true. For no good reason, I felt uneasy for him, as though he had sent me disquieting, instead of good, news. If I was a believer in the supernatural I should call it a premonition; as I am not I will merely say that it was due to my inherent inability to believe in unalloyed good fortune.

Chapter Twelve

A PROMISE REDEEMED

It had never crossed my mind that I should ever again play an active, personal part in the affairs of Giovanni Campo. I had done so once, when the Fascists had struck at him, and from that connexion had sprung a friendship that was now bearing fruit in a voluminous correspondence from the remote distances of China—a correspondence that, even in those days, I felt might provide the material for a book if ever I should find the time and inclination to write it. That it should happen again was beyond the probabilities. I doubted if I should ever see him any more in the flesh; but in any event his paths and mine lay far apart and were never likely to cross.

If, as the mathematicians tell us, there are laws of probability, they do not seem to apply to human affairs, for the improbable is just as likely to happen as the probable. The chances against my intervening directly into Giovanni's life must have been so vast as to make the occurrence an impossibility; but it happened all the same. So it is that to continue the story of Giovanni Campo, it is necessary to return once more to Florence. The odd thing is that, if these events which I am about to record had been timed a month later, I should not have been there, for I was about to leave Italy for good—a thought which leads to some disturbing reflections on Fate.

My own affairs do not concern this story much, but it is just as well to set down that I had not done too badly in

141

Germany, despite the growing difficulties which Nazi doctrines placed upon the activities of those who were neither Germans nor Nazis. At any rate I had gained all I could in knowledge and felt that if I was to make any sort of career I must transfer myself to a larger field. Already my eyes were turning towards England. True, Germany still was the Mecca of all who would reach the heights in surgery. But strange things were happening in Germany, and it looked as if the position of foreigners there might become even worse than it was in Italy.

Fascism had now complete and undisputed sway in Italy, as it had had for years, but stability did not bring moderation or toleration. On the contrary, it grew more and more rigorous, searching ever for the traitor or independent-minded person on whom it might work its wrath. No one was safe from the informer or the displeasure of the local leader and his cronies. Indeed, even the leaders themselves were not safe. None of them knew when the accusing finger might not be pointed at them and their brief reign of authority brought to a sudden and unpleasant end.

In Florence, Buonsanti had been a power, and it has to be admitted that at first he had done some good things for the city. It was more orderly, better served, cleaner. But those were only superficials. Beneath the external beauty and order there was stinking corruption, and if there was less crime in the ordinary civilized sense there was never a time when the murderer's knife was allowed freer play—provided that the hand wielding it belonged to a man in a black shirt.

Buonsanti had been in command long enough to have made many enemies. His victims, the non-Fascists, he could afford to ignore. He could not be so indifferent to the foes within the Party. In a sense, he had been too successful. Personal prestige and popularity are dangers to members of all totalitarian regimes in which men's loyalties must be focused on one person and one person alone—the leader. For all that, Buonsanti appeared to be sufficiently well established in the favour of the higher authorities of Fascism to be quite secure; any threat to him could come only from above. That was an outsider's view. How wrong it was was revealed to me in a strange and sensational manner.

I still considered Florence as my home because my parents had moved there and I spent all my holidays with them. We had our own flat, and we were blessed with our own front door. No longer had I perforce to share in the lives of my neighbours. Having made a final note or two to an article I was preparing for publication, I rose, stretched myself, and decided I had done enough for one day. And at that moment there was a knock at the door. It was a timid knock, as though its maker did not wish to disturb the neighbours. I sighed and cursed softly. Who it could be, I had no idea. Visitors to our flat were rare—unknown at this hour of the night; and since I was not practising in Florence it could hardly be one of those patients who invariably choose the most inconvenient times for crises in their ailments. But there was just a chance that someone had been looking for a doctor, been unable to find one, and been directed to our door. This reflection smothered the half-formed intention to ignore the knock—though I think in any case my curiosity would have forced me to open the door if there had been a second summons.

I was quite unprepared to find a woman on the threshold. She was muffled up to the eyes, though the night was oppressively warm—it was the heat, in fact, that had driven me to abandon my writing at an unusually early hour. But it was not that curious fact which most interested me. There was something familiar about this inopportune visitor, but rack my brains though I might, I could not recognize her so disguised.

She did not wait for me to speak, but stepped rapidly into the little passage—it could hardly be called a hall—and softly closed the door behind her. I was too astonished at this conduct to do or say anything, and confined myself to a stare that was both incredulous and rude.

'Dr. Sava,' she said in a voice thickly muffled by the scarf wrapped round the lower part of her face, 'I want to speak to you—privately. No one must know I am here, so talk softly.'

Despite myself I smiled slightly. This was too melodramatic for words. The muffled woman coming unasked into my rooms at this late hour, speaking in disguised tones, and urging on me, even before I knew her identity, the need for secrecy, was straight out of one of the less intellectual type of thriller.

She saw my smile. 'It is serious,' she went on. 'Desperate!'

The voice was vaguely familiar as her appearance had been to me. Though her last words had deepened the artificial air of melodrama, I was no longer amused. After all, Fascist Italy lived in a perpetual state of melodrama.

'Do I know you?' I asked. 'You seem rather familiar, but I cannot place you. But come in here,' I said, leading the way. 'As for keeping quiet'—I could not resist the thrust—'I am not likely to advertise the fact that I entertain ladies at this hour in my flat. My parents are excellent in many ways, but their sense of propriety is very strict. I can't give a bad impression to my young sisters, either!'

She paid no attention to this sally, but slowly, and with hands that trembled slightly as though she was in serious terror, unwrapped the scarf from her face. And then I knew her. It was Lydia Buonsanti. If I had stopped to think clearly for a moment, I might have guessed it.

'Signorina Buonsanti!' I exclaimed softly. 'What brings you here?' As I spoke I felt I knew the answer to my question, though it was probably not the one she would give. Nothing but trouble could bring her to me, whom she had so despised.

A Promise Redeemed

'I—we—that is to say, my father and I are in serious trouble,' she answered, 'and I have come here, Dr. Sava, on the strength of an old friendship, to ask for help.'

'I am by no means an important person,' I pointed out. 'I do not know if I can help, or even whether I ought to give any help I might, until I know your trouble. Tell me.'

'It is the Party, doctor,' she continued. 'Father has been proscribed. The Grand Council themselves have decreed that he must go. Their decision won't be announced till tomorrow at the earliest. But luckily we have one or two friends left and they have given us warning.'

'I see. On what grounds is this happening?'

'On none,' she said scornfully, her eyes flashing darkly. 'It is a trumped-up charge to get rid of father. He is too popular and a potential danger to the higher leadership— a dangerous man, they say. That is all.'

'Ah!' I could not help smiling sardonically. 'So now it has come home to the hangman, eh? And the hangman is not too pleased about it.'

She drew herself up haughtily.

'Dr. Sava, this is no time for trying to score off me and making cheap gibes,' she said coldly. 'I know you dislike me—perhaps despise me—but I am a woman in trouble and I am asking for your protection.'

'Even if,' I returned, 'that protection involves for me and my parents the fate to which you feel you are condemned?'

'How hard you are!' she sighed, and a tear glistened in her black eyes. 'How hard—and how cold!'

I was young. I was impressionable. Lydia was beautiful; and it is difficult to resist the tears of a beautiful woman.

'I am sorry, signorina,' I said quickly and warmly. 'You are right to remind me that I am behaving disgracefully.'

She smiled tearfully.

'Thank you, doctor,' she returned. 'I was sure that your real self would break through sooner or later. I do not deny that I have earned your scorn, for last time you saw me—you remember?—I behaved no better towards you.'

'Tell me,' I pressed, 'why have you come to me? Why do you think I can help you?'

'You shielded Giovanni—dear Giovanni!—in his moment of danger, when even I had to deny him,' she replied, in a tone that almost convinced me of her sincerity; or it may be that the memory of her tears still lingered. 'You are brave, doctor, and resourceful. But,' she added quickly, for I believe I looked a little aghast at the prospect of harbouring a woman wanted by the Fascisti, 'I am not going to ask you to do anything like that for me. I have had this warning, and I can escape to Switzerland. But even there I know I shall not be safe. I need someone to protect me.'

'Your father?' I suggested.

She closed her eyes. 'My father has the opportunity but he does not choose to escape,' she replied with a touch of pride in her voice. 'He is a brave man and will face all the lies they bring up against him. He has nothing of which he need feel ashamed or guilty. I have begged him to go while he may but he refuses. I would remain by his side but he refuses. He says'—she lowered her head—'he would shoot me rather than that they should insult me.'

'I see,' I remarked, somewhat overcome by this highly dramatic outburst. 'Then what can I do?'

'Listen,' she said intently. 'I cannot remain unprotected. I need help. I ask you one thing, doctor—one simple thing which I believe you have the power to supply. Where is Giovanni?'

I almost leapt from my skin, for that question came with the crack of a whiplash.

'Giovanni?' I repeated. It was incredible that she should ask.

She nodded. 'Yes, he will help me. I know it. He loved me once and he has never ceased to love me. I will go to him wherever he is. You know his address. Tell me.'

I shook my head. 'I do not know,' I replied.

It was true. I had had no word from Giovanni since he had announced his new appointment and his forthcoming departure for Jehol. A letter sent to him might waste months wandering about China. As it was, when I knew his exact address, the letter had taken a very long time in transit.

She looked at me disbelievingly. 'But surely you know. Is he still in Africa?'

I looked up sharply. It was, of course, the first time I knew that she had had that anonymous letter, the writing of which had bothered me so much, and I was thrown off my guard.

'So you got my note?' I murmured.

'It was you who sent it then?' She nodded slightly to herself. 'Yes, you were his friend and would do anything he asked, no matter what the cost. But you are not *my* friend. You are my enemy, because you think I deserted him when he was in need and danger. That was no fault of mine. No other course was open to me. But do not lie to me, doctor. I am sure you know where he is. He would want you to let me know, I am certain.'

That was precisely the point that was worrying me. He had made me promise, almost with the last words I had spoken to him, that I would cable him if ever I learnt that Lydia was in trouble. Yet how could I do it? I did not trust her. She was only turning to him now because all else had failed. Her dreams of greatness and success among the rich and powerful Fascisti had come to an end with dramatic suddenness. The noose her father had so often dangled before others was opening for him—and perhaps her, too, for it was quite on the cards that she might have compromised some of the leaders—and all her so-called allies of yesterday were now her sworn enemies. Woman-like she knew of her power over Giovanni, sensed that he had gone to Africa to be away from her, and now proposed to use that power ruthlessly.

Giovanni was my friend. He had suffered much already, both on account of this very woman and for other things that were no true fault of his. The last letter I had had announced the realization of his dreams. He was set now on the path to the success he would himself have chosen from among all others possible to him. Yet I was convinced that if she called to him he would give it all up, abandon the position he had won, desert what he regarded as his life's work. For what? Would it be no more than the fickle embraces of a woman who, when her immediate danger had passed, would at once desert him for some bigger, more glittering prize?

She was looking at me with a curious expression that held both pleading and scorn. I turned my head to avoid it.

There was my promise. If Giovanni ever came to know that I had broken it, that I had, by deliberate choice, denied him the chance of hearing from her, even being with her, our friendship would be over and I should earn his undying hatred. Of that I was assured.

I think she must have read something of the conflict that was going on in me, if she did not know its precise nature. Suddenly I found her close to me, putting her hands on my breast and looking up at me.

'George,' she said. I thought she had forgotten the name she had used so often in the old days of my studentship. 'George, be careful what you do. I believe I know what you are thinking—you feel you ought to protect your friend from my evil influence. But you do not know all the truth, at any rate on my side. Have you the right, George,' she continued in a lower, cajoling voice, 'to stand between him and me? Remember he loves me still—you know that as I know it—and perhaps I—I love him too.'

She dropped her eyes which had been large and pleading

when they had been turned on me. Her bosom heaved a little.

Still I could not answer. Perhaps the highest expression I could give to my friendship for Giovanni was to deny that friendship, to break my promise, and yet. . . .

'Well?' she said, becoming slightly scornful again, 'haven't you even the courage to repeat your refusal?'

'I have not refused, Lydia,' I said, using her Christian name deliberately in an effort to be candid. 'I told you the truth when I said I did not know his address. He went to China well over a year ago. I have not heard from him for several weeks now, but in his last letter he told me he was being moved to a new station in a different part of the country. I could not get in touch with him if I tried. Until I hear again from him, I do not know where he is.'

It was a stupid thing to say. My whole being told me I was being weak and foolish, allowing myself to be bewitched by this woman, this Circe, this Tamara, almost as Giovanni had been. But curiously when I had finished I felt infinitely lighter in mind and spirit as though a burden had been lifted from me. I could almost hear Giovanni's words of thanks and approval in my ears.

'That is the truth?' she asked.

I nodded. My last defences were down. She and my promise to Giovanni had broken all my strength of rational will.

'Yes,' I said. 'That is the truth. If you like I will show you his letter.'

'No,' she said shaking her head, 'I believe you, all the more because you gave me the information reluctantly. So Giovanni is in China. What am I to do now?'

Suddenly the pose of self-control and determination vanished. In her eyes, when she looked at me, there was sheer, naked terror. From the sophisticated woman playing for some stake she wanted she had become the most pathetic sight of all, a woman faced with a danger she dreads and feeling utterly deserted by her friends, with nowhere to go, no one to turn to for comfort. It was too much for me.

'Listen, Lydia,' I said quickly but sincerely, 'there is no need to be alarmed. You are right. Giovanni would want to know about this. I will tell you what to do. Go to Switzerland as soon as you can. Let me know your address as soon as you have found somewhere to live. Giovanni will write to me—he writes very often and I am sure it will not be long before I hear again. I will send you his address at once and you can write to him.'

My brain told me I was a fool; my heart told me I could not do otherwise.

'Thank you,' she replied, growing calmer. 'Thank you, George. It is wonderful to think there is someone left to help me.'

'I am Giovanni's friend, and I know he would want me to help you. That is enough in itself,' I said, a little embarrassed. 'But you must not waste a moment. You have a ticket, passport, money?'

'Yes. I have those—while they are any good to me.'

'And the next train?'

'It is early in the morning. I shall walk outside the town and pick it up at another station. It is slow.'

'I will hire a taxi,' I suggested. 'Would you like me to travel with you?'

There is no depth of folly to which a man moved by a pretty woman, even one he hates and despises, will not sink. Perhaps if I had remained cold, hard, and rational, Giovanni's life would have been different. Perhaps . . . But what is the good of saying 'perhaps'? Better to ask, I think, whether Giovanni would have wished it to be otherwise? Though it fell out as it did, I do not think he would have regretted, or ever did regret, the course it took.

She was shaking her head in answer to my question.

'There will be fewer questions if I travel alone,' she said quietly. 'But I am grateful to you all the same.'

'Then let us go at once. I will see about a car.'

I could have knocked up a friend and borrowed his—but it would have been suspicious. The romantic Italian taxi-drivers would not argue or notice anything at all surprising if a young man wanted to drive into the night with a woman who, though her face was muffled, was obviously attractive. They might even invoke blessings on us, their minds filled with sentimental visions. . . .

It was twenty-five miles to the station she thought would be safe, where she believed she would be un-recognized; for it would have been difficult for the notorious Lydia Buonsanti to leave Florence without comment, even in disguise. I paid off the taxi, not counting the cost, though how I was going to return to Florence I did not know—or care. It was an adventure tinged with romance. And I repeat that I was still young.

It was two hours before the train was due, and we sheltered in a decrepit barn, nestling close together for warmth. The pressure of her body sent a hot thrill through me, and perhaps then, as never before or since, I could fully understand Giovanni's pitiful obsession for this woman. She was one of those strange, enigmatic creatures whom one can love and hate at the same time, who have but to ask of a man and he gives his all, sacrificing every-thing, and regretting only that he had not more to give. In that moment, too, I envied Giovanni.

She was a sorceress.

I saw her off, resisting the last-minute impulse to spring into the carriage beside her and plead for permission to follow her wherever she might go. And when at last I found myself again in Florence, I felt dejected and hopeless, wondering why life had so little to offer.

A week later I heard from her. Her letter was full of profuse gratitude for what I had done. I was her true and beloved friend. And she begged me not to forget to write as soon as I heard from Giovanni. She was no longer near me. The spell of the midnight meeting had passed. Once again I was calling myself a fool, even a traitor to Giovanni's better interests. But the die was cast. I could not draw back now. As if to emphasize the fact, the next post brought me a letter from Giovanni, telling me his new address and asking for my latest news. He spoke of how busy he was and how high his hopes were running. Like a man condemned to sign a false recantation, I sat down and sent the address to Lydia.

Chapter Thirteen

THE SURPRISE RETURN

Lydia had made her escape only just in time. The day after she left her father was arrested as he sat working in his office and was removed to Rome 'for examination and trial by the Grand Council'. Florence never heard of him again. The charges against him were never published and the proceedings—if in fact there were any—were *in camera*. All that is known definitely about him is that he was shot. Florence passed under the control of a chief of the typical Fascist type—the man who believes that ruthless bullying is an indication of strength and character.

The whole affair had left me dejected and restless. I was glad that very soon I should be leaving Italy for good and that its rather too dramatic life would become only memories to me. The thought that I had allowed myself to be bewitched by Lydia and had done Giovanni a bad turn inconsistent with the true friendship and regard I felt for him tormented me. Once I sat down and wrote an exceptionally long letter, telling him not only of what had occurred but also of my doubts as to its wisdom. I tore it up. There was no point in creating more trouble where enough—or the seeds for it—existed already. Instead, I rewrote a simple note giving him the facts and expressing the hope that I had acted as he wished, though I tried to phrase that expression in such a way as would reveal my doubts to him. It was the best I could do. I resigned myself to waiting for his answer with such patience as I could command. No doubt it would be a matter of months before I heard, even though both of us regularly used the air mail. The journey up country wasted an immense amount of time.

My work in Florence was now over and I had resolved to spend a short time in taking a long-delayed and much-needed holiday in Switzerland. Lydia was in Zürich, so I planned my itinerary to avoid that charming town. There was plenty to see and do elsewhere in the country, and, as a matter of fact, I proposed to spend as much of my time as possible away from the larger centres. It would be a change to be alone for a little while. Nevertheless, I felt I was under some sort of obligation to Lydia because of Giovanni's interest in her and the promise I had made to her, so, as soon as my arrangements were made, I sent her the address of a friend of mine in Basle through which she could, in emergency, reach me.

In the five weeks that followed I forgot all about Lydia and her troubles, nor did I think much about Giovanni. My mind grew more restful and my recent stupidities no longer worried me. I climbed mountains, boated on those incredibly blue and peaceful lakes, and generally escaped from the harsh realities of life. It was only to be expected, therefore, that I should be brought back to them with something of a shock.

The fuse that set off the explosion came, as it so often does, in the form of a telegram, which I found waiting for me on one of my periodical returns to my friend's house in Basle, which I was using as a base. My friend, Ludwig Hascher, had been a little worried about it, for he had not known whether to send it on to me or leave it to await my return, which I had announced in a hurried note. I arrived in the evening; it had been delivered in the morning.

The mere sight of it set unwelcome thoughts surging through my head. It brought back everything I had so successfully forgotten during the past happy weeks of holiday-making. For it was obvious to me that it could come only from Lydia, since she was almost the only person who had my address, and Lydia, I was now convinced, was not likely to communicate with me unless she had some new trouble for me. My eyes almost started from my head when I had torn open the envelope and read the message inside:

'Come at once. Urgent. Lydia's address. Giovanni.'

For a moment or two I was too dumbfounded to think at all. Then my first reaction was that it could be nothing more nor less than a hoax. Giovanni was in China and it was a physical impossibility for him to be sending telegrams from Zürich to me. Yet who was likely to hoax me? I could not suspect Lydia. If she wanted me she knew she would not have to resort to the use of Giovanni's name. It was beyond understanding—utterly and completely inexplicable.

I shrugged and turned to Ludwig. 'I can't understand this at all,' I said, showing him the telegram, 'but on the face of it it looks as though a friend of mine who I thought was thousands of miles away in China has turned up in Zürich and wants to see me urgently. I suppose I'd better go as soon as I can.'

He could not help me, except in the very practical way of telling me the times of trains. I left that evening.

In Zürich I had some difficulty in finding Lydia's address. It was in one of the shabbier backstreets—not at all the sort of place I should have expected the glamorous Lydia Buonsanti, erstwhile toast of the Fascist Party, to choose. But perhaps Fascist officials and their families cannot take so much with them when they flee as did the in-and-out Chinese governors of whom Giovanni had written to me.

The house turned out to be even poorer than I expected, and when I knocked the door was answered by a fat German-Swiss woman with four children, the eldest no more than six years of age, surrounding her.

'Fräulein Buonsanti?' she said. 'Another gentleman visitor? I shall raise her rent if this goes on. Third floor, mein Herr. Go up and knock on the first door to the left of the staircase.' She shrugged and spread her plump hands.

'It is no fault of mine if the gentleman already there throws you down the stairs again. All I ask is that you do not damage my house.'

I mounted the stairs gingerly. They creaked at every step and they were far from well lighted. At the third floor I paused. The affair had suddenly taken on an air of sordidness I did not like; but it would have been foolish to turn back now, and so I knocked, as directed, at the first door on the left, under which a thin stream of light was leaking.

There was a short pause, and then the door was thrown open. Lydia peered out at me, her expression far from welcoming. And she was a very different Lydia. She had lost all her air of smartness and sophistication; she looked unwashed and unkempt and had, in fact, the air of a rather unsavoury trollop. But she smiled when she saw who her visitor was.

'Why, George!' she exclaimed. 'Come in. So you got Giovanni's telegram and came at once. How good of you—and how like you! He's not here at the moment, but he's coming along shortly. Sit down and I'll make you a cup of coffee. If you've come straight from the train, you will need something.'

I sank into a chair and looked about me. It was the shabbiest of shabby rooms. I have lived in some queer and cheap places myself, but I had never had anything like this. My rooms, for all their faults, had always been tolerably clean; this, frankly, was filthy. It was also untidy to the point of chaos. A cupboard door stood open revealing inside a disorder almost unbelievable. The chair I had taken was the only one that had not something thrown down on it. On the floor was a dress, which looked as if it had been left there when Lydia had stepped out of it. The bed in the corner had been simply pulled up; it was not even covered by the counterpane, which lay in a heap on the floor near the foot.

'I'm afraid I'm in a bit of a mess,' she remarked as she busied herself in the corner with the coffee percolator. 'I haven't had time to clear up, and it's so difficult to manage on one's own with only one room.'

'That's all right,' I returned. 'But tell me about Giovanni. How on earth did he get here? My letter can barely have reached him yet. Besides, I thought he was in China.'

She smiled triumphantly. 'Oh, that's really quite simple,' she replied, 'though I suppose it is a bit surprising when you don't know the facts. As soon as I got your letter with his address, I cabled Giovanni asking him to come as I was in grave trouble. He did—that's all. He flew most of the way.'

I stared at her in complete astonishment. She had done all that—used her power over him to make him leave his work, Heaven knew at what cost, and she could talk about it as though it was the most natural thing in the world, like asking a neighbour for a jug of water because the water-pipes in one's house have burst. I had to fight the rage that swelled up in me, for I felt like giving her a good hearty spanking and walking out of the room. Luckily for me and her, for I do not think I could have remained even civil, Giovanni came in at that moment.

He stared at me open-eyed and open-mouthed; and then he rushed towards me and embraced me.

'George!' he cried. 'George! Here so soon! Isn't it marvellous, Lydia? George is here!'

I disengaged myself from his rapturous welcome.

'Well, it's good to see you again, Giovanni,' I said. 'But it isn't I who've turned up in Switzerland from China almost overnight. I thought at first that telegram might be a hoax.'

'No, I'm here, as you see. We want you, George. Lydia and I want you. We're going to ask you to help us again, you see.'

'Oh?' I did not sound at all enthusiastic. I wished, in fact, that I had listened to Giovanni's earlier pleadings and buried myself in the most remote and inaccessible part of Central Africa where it would be impossible to become involved in friends' affairs.

'Nothing difficult this time, George,' he went on, with the same sort of irresponsible gaiety, which was quite abnormal to him. 'We want you to help us to get married."

'Married?' I exclaimed.

He nodded excitedly. 'Yes, George. Isn't it wonderful? Married. You don't think I'd come all the way from China for nothing, do you?' And he laughed.

'Don't be so silly,' Lydia interposed. She was smiling on him and I could see that he was utterly at her mercy. 'You're behaving like some schoolboy with his first girl. It's true, George,' she added, turning to me. 'We're going to get married, and then we're going back together to China.'

The world was turning itself upside down. My thoughts were reeling. I sprang to my feet.

'Quiet, both of you!' I almost shouted. 'I don't know whether I'm on my head or my heels. I shall wake up in a moment and find this is some mad dream. I was hoping to have a letter from you and now I find you here and about to marry Lydia.'

'I'll tell you everything,' he said rapidly. 'I can scarcely believe it myself I'm so happy. Now. . . '

Lydia held up a restraining hand. 'Not now, Giovanni. I've got George's coffee ready, but I expect he's hungry as well after his journey and I've nothing to give him, except some rolls. So let him drink it in peace and then you can take him out to dinner, and you two can talk to your hearts' content. I expect you'll have a lot to say to each other. Besides, I'm tired and want to go to bed.'

'Of course, darling. You must be tired.' Giovanni had obviously forgotten my very presence. 'I'll go at once.'

'Let George have his coffee first,' she said.

'Yes, yes. Of course. George and I will go out to dinner the moment he's finished.'

I was not sorry to leave a few minutes later. Perhaps

in the more public atmosphere of a restaurant, Giovanni might show some signs of his more normal self. At the moment he was quite incomprehensible. Lydia had been right. He was like a schoolboy—or, in that charming English phrase, a dog with two tails.

My hopes were not disappointed. Removed from Lydia's proximity, Giovanni subsided into taciturn gloom; he might have just said farewell to her for ever. He left me to choose the restaurant, and, later, the meal, and seemed utterly uninterested in the whole proceedings.

'Now,' I said, when he had desultorily pecked at his food, 'tell me all about it. I want a clear consistent story, if you're capable of it. And I want to know how all this happened.'

He sipped some wine.

'Yes, George,' he said meekly. 'I'm sorry. But the moment Lydia is out of my sight, I feel absolutely lost. I've spent so much of my life away from her. You've never been in love, George—not real love. I know you've been attracted to certain girls, but that's not love, George. I couldn't live any longer without Lydia.'

I refrained from pointing out that this seemed more like a desperate melodramatic passion than true love. Silence is golden.

'But I must tell you all about it,' he went on. 'It's all so simple. I was just moving into the new station when I got her cablegram. Of course I was overjoyed to hear from her—even to think that she remembered me and called to me when she wanted help. I knew that in her heart she always loved me, however Fate might make her take a different course. No, you didn't believe that, George, I know, but this proves it.'

Again I stopped myself from making the obvious, biting comment of any port in a storm.

'Give me the facts,' I said sternly. 'You can talk about Lydia afterwards.'

'Yes—George. That's what I'm trying to do. She asked me to come to Zürich as she was in great trouble. Of course, she couldn't say what. So I went to the President —how lucky it was he'd travelled with me to help in the preparation of the station!—and told him a very dear friend of mine in Europe was in grave trouble and I had to go at once. These business men are strange people, George. They don't think of the important things of life. He stared at me as though I was mad, and he even had the cheek to say that Switzerland was a long way off from China—as though I didn't know it. He argued quite a lot and got quite nasty about it.'

'Perhaps that's understandable,' I commented.

'Oh yes, but there are other things in life than business or even medicine,' he retorted. 'You realize that when you're in love. So I told him that I had to go, and if I couldn't have leave, he could have my resignation. After all that only meant appointing a new Chief. I hadn't done any real work in establishing the station. Someone else would have been glad of the job.'

'You said that?' I asked in astonishment.

He nodded. 'What else could I say?'

'You were ready to throw up everything merely on the strength of that cable, without knowing what sort of trouble Lydia was in? It might have been something quite trivial and she'd sent it to you in a moment of hysteria. . . .'

'Don't be silly, George,' he cried. 'How could any of Lydia's troubles be trivial to me? If she wanted me, I had no choice but to go. I didn't want anything else. And in the end the President agreed, but he said I must be back in four months at the outside, otherwise he would dismiss me, and find someone else. After that he got quite helpful and arranged air travel for me. The Americans are wonderful at that sort of thing. And well—here I am.'

'I see. And what are you proposing to do now? Oh, yes, I know you and Lydia are going to get married. But what then?'

'She's going back to China with me. That's quite in order. There are quite a few married men on the stations.'

The Surprise Return

'Lydia's agreed to go to China?' I asked, stupefied.

He nodded excitedly. 'Of course. She wants to be with me. Where else? I told her I'd readily look for another job in Europe if she preferred, but she said no, she'd rather be with me where I thought my work lay.'

'It's all so amazing I can't grasp it yet,' I remarked. That Lydia should consent to live in China was beyond my comprehension. Perhaps I unjustly suspected her, but I could not help feeling that something lay behind this—something that Giovanni, in his utter infatuation, would not see even if it were pointed out to him.

'Well, it's true,' he returned, and then he leant towards me, a serious expression on his face. 'George, I can't say how grateful Lydia and I are to you for all you've done. You've given us the greatest happiness in the world. I can never thank you, even if I live to be a hundred. You saved my life once, and now you've given me a new life of a kind I dared not hope for.'

'Forget about that,' I said. I meant it. I wanted to forget it, for I had an uneasy conviction that I would have done better, perhaps, to let Giovanni die at the hands of the Fascists all those years ago. I did not trust Lydia.

Till our meal was ended—and he protracted it inordinately—he talked of nothing but Lydia. No powers of mine were enough to check his headlong rush. He told me of her beauty, her charm, her self-sacrifice, her devotion. Her life, he told me, had been one long agony. But now he was going to make her forget all she had suffered, to strive to give her the happiness she so richly deserved. . . . It went on and on and on till I was on the point of screaming.

Giovanni the lover was beyond all explanation or understanding. He lost every one of those qualities which made him so outstanding in everything else he did. His finely balanced judgment, his detestation of fraud and falsity, his serenity of mind—all these and many other fine traits were submerged beneath a flood of idolatry. That is the one just word. Lydia was his goddess.

Nothing she could do or say would ever be wrong or even suspect in his eyes. Such adoration is, no doubt, wonderful, an inexplicable expression of the depths that are in the human spirit. Yet also it is the most dangerous state into which a man may fall—and especially a brilliant man like Giovanni. Giovanni's strength and distinction lay in his ability to trust himself and his judgment; with those bound to another—and Lydia of all people—he might so easily become lost and confused. I feared for the future.

When we parted I think it was the first time I had ever been glad to say goodbye to him. He had said nothing of his work or his plans. All that was, indeed, forgotten. Now his one plan was to devote himself to Lydia. I tried to think no more of it.

The wedding had already been arranged. It was to take place in ten days' time, and then the two were to fly to Cairo for a short honeymoon, after which they would set out by air for China. Of course, I had to stay for the wedding, where I had been cast for the composite role of groomsman, chief witness, and bride's guardian—a somewhat exacting combination. And once I found myself alone with Lydia. I turned to her, my curiosity overcoming my determination to have as little to do with this unsavoury business as I could.

'How do you like the idea of going to China, Lydia?' I asked, trying to make my question sound as casual as possible.

She smiled. 'I think I shall like it, George. I hate leaving Europe for some things, but it has advantages, you know, quite apart from being with Giovanni.' The insincerity I thought I detected in that remark was probably the outcome of my biased outlook. 'You see, I'm not really safe here. It's too near Italy and—well, I'm not popular any longer with the Fascists. I know too much. Even in Switzerland people have been kidnapped, you know, or even murdered. I don't want to be a prisoner or a corpse, you know. Beyond that, you see, it would be very difficult for Giovanni to do anything in Europe.

He'd have to start all over again, and I've seen enough of poverty in this room'—we were in that depressing apartment of hers—'to want no more of it. He's got a good position in China, and I shan't have to kow-tow to anyone particularly. There are other opportunities waiting for him that I'll help him to get if I can. You see, George, I'd rather be the wife of a somebody in China than a nobody in Europe. You probably think that cold and mercenary of me, but it's true. And Giovanni's so much in love with me that he'll make a perfect husband.'

She spoke coolly and deliberately, and I felt for the first time that she was speaking the truth as much as it was possible to do so. She wanted position and security. Giovanni could offer her those in China and add to them an unquestioning, unfailing devotion that would feed the voracious fires of her vanity. It was a good bargain, and now that she had nothing to lose in Europe, it appealed to her.

'I see,' I said slowly. 'I hope you'll both be very happy.'

'I'm sure we shall.'

It was only when I was returning from the airport after seeing off the newly married pair that I realized I had been nearly a fortnight with Giovanni and knew no more about his work, his plans, and his ambitions, than he had told me in his letters. He had spent every moment he could with Lydia, and the odd occasions on which I saw him he devoted to extolling her charms and virtues. Giovanni had become, in fact, a bore—and a bore in love is a most distressing phenomenon. The plane was already lost to view, I doubted if I should hear much more of Giovanni. If he did write, it would merely be about Lydia.

PART THREE

Chapter Fourteen

FIRST SHOTS

No news was to come from Giovanni for a very long time, and as the silent weeks passed by the doubts I had already formed whether I should ever hear from him again were strengthened. At the end of the twenties and the beginning of the thirties, psychology was very much the vogue, and, in common with most doctors of my generation, I had plumbed fairly deeply into its turgid streams. It seemed to me the most natural thing in the world to seek in the fashionable theories some explanation of Giovanni Campo's queer behaviour, which was surely not motivated by pure reason. So I had come to the conclusion—which seems laughable now but then had an air of profundity—that in these past few years I had served as a substitute satisfaction to my friend, played the role of an object onto which he could divert his unrewarded craving for Lydia. From this it followed that now he had at last won his Lydia, I had served my turn and could expect, at most, no more than the casual letters one receives from friends abroad in far places. Of course my conjectures were quite wrong, as they so often are when a man has tried to use the shifting sands of psychological theory as a firm foundation for prediction.

But my thoughts of Giovanni were not devoted entirely to this sort of intellectual acrobatics. I had ample time to consider his affairs in an objective way; and the more the cold light of reason was turned on them, the more extraordinary they appeared. It was barely credible that a man of his intellectual stature and professional ambition should hazard the whole of his career and prospects, and travel half-way round the world at the mere suggestion of a woman who had, in his hour of need, ostentatiously turned her back on him and thereafter treated him with the most contemptuous of silences—a woman who had, moreover, publicly and enthusiastically embraced causes he abhorred and consorted openly with men whom he had himself often described as murderers and gangsters. His actions were surprising enough; but even more astonishing was the fact that apparently he could see nothing at all out of the way in them.

In its way, Lydia's conduct was hardly less puzzling. That she might, in suitable circumstances, make use of Giovanni's blind devotion to her to serve her own ends was no more than might have been expected from what I knew of her. She was a woman who would, in my view, employ anyone and anything for her advantage, and shame or embarrassment would not hold her back. But that she should voluntarily abandon Europe and its promises and prospects for her, and elect to accompany Giovanni to China was almost beyond belief.

China in general, and a medical mission station in that country in particular, offered no particular attraction to a white woman at any time, and I suppose the majority of white women outside the bigger Westernized towns of the coast were those who were themselves doctors or missionaries or nurses, filled with an urge to human service. Lydia had, so far as I knew, none of those qualifications, either of character or of competence. I doubt whether the horizon of her ambition had ever extended further than the higher social circles of Fascist Rome. But at the opening of the fourth decade of this century, the winds of trouble were beginning to howl ominously in the Far East, and no place could, on the face of it, have appealed less to a woman of Lydia's temperament.

Japan had already invaded Manchuria and established her puppet state of Manchukuo, from which she was reaching out into the adjoining provinces of China. The League of Nations, to which the matter had been referred by China, had shown nothing but an enthusiasm to run away from the problem and dodge its responsibilities; and with each new manifestation of international weakness, vacillation, and procrastination, the truculence of Japan's war lords mounted. All this is ancient history now, dimmed by the blaze of the world war that followed inevitably—for who can doubt that its real beginnings were in Manchukuo, Spain, and Abyssinia?—but the events need recalling for they had a very direct bearing on Giovanni's career, which I am trying to record here in these pages.

It was not simply that he was in China, and therefore anything that affected Chinese affairs must indirectly react on him. He had gone—and Lydia with him—to Jehol, one of the north-eastern provinces next to Manchukuo, from which already came reports of fighting and what was later to be known as infiltration. If the 'Manchukuo Incident', as it was called, should develop, Jehol was likely to be a highly dangerous spot.

News of all this was familiar to European newspaper readers even while Giovanni was in Zürich waiting to marry Lydia; and he, fresh from China, must surely have been more aware of the implications than I or anyone living in Europe could have been. It was true he never mentioned them, but that was in tune with the whole business; he had been so wrapped up in his own personal affairs that nothing else had mattered or been worth discussing. Here was another detailed problem within the major one. There had already been suggestions that white women should be evacuated from the centre of trouble; why, then, did Giovanni take the risk of transporting his bride there? All my thoughts led me nowhere. From beginning to end the whole situation was utterly inexplicable; and as, by now, I had abandoned all hope of hearing again from Giovanni, I decided it was a mystery to which I should never find the solution.

Giovanni's first letter, when at last it came, threw no light on that problem though it did indicate the seriousness of affairs in the north-eastern provinces.

'The situation', he wrote, 'is full of surprises and it looks as though things may get a great deal worse. I had learnt to accept bandits and minor wars as part of the normal state of affairs in China but this business is something quite different. The Japs are a foreign invader. Of course, there's no real war. I doubt if there ever will be, and probably it will all end by the Japs quietly taking over the province as they have taken Manchukuo. Quite a lot of people think that would be a good thing, for at any rate they do something about organization and government. . . .'

This last remark suggested that he had travelled some distance from the views that had led to his becoming an anti-Fascist leader in his university days, though it was true that he did not endorse it. Naturally, there was news of Lydia:

'Lydia has settled down here wonderfully well, and won instant popularity with the other people on the station. Everyone admires her to such an extent that at times I grow intensely jealous! Everyone, too, praises her for her courage in coming out here at this time and thinks it remarkable. But then they don't know Lydia as I do and have no idea of her immense courage in the face of adversity. . . .'

He was still in his state of illusion about Lydia, then. And also, which was more surprising, he still seemed to have no realistic view of the dangers that beset her, as they did all of them out there in Jehol. The next letter, a little later, showed, however, that events were at last beginning to have their influence on his outlook:

'Things really are serious here,' he wrote. 'I had no idea that matters were so grave. Naturally I have to travel about the country quite a lot, and though I use a truck when I can, there are more often than not no roads to take me where I want to go, so it is pioneer overland travel by foot or litter. On these journeys one is rarely out of earshot of rifle fire. One is quite as likely to meet a Japanese or Manchukuo soldier as natives of the province. Most of the Chinese belong to the Communist organizations, which are very strong up here, and they, as I expect you know, are far from being friends with the Central Nationalist Government.

'Some of the stories that reach me are almost incredible until I remember that this is China, not Europe, and sometimes we, as bystanders seeing most of the game, are forced to wonder whether the Central Government want more to get rid of the Communists or the Japs. A little while ago I had to make an upcountry trip that took me almost to the Manchukuo border, which was not a very attractive proposition. I left Lydia behind, of course, though she begged me to let her come. She says she can't bear to be parted from me for a moment, but I felt it was rather too dangerous even for her, and she is quite safe on the station.

'We walked into what I can only describe as a minor battle. There was a small body of Jap troops on the road, and they were being heavily harassed by the Chinese guerillas, who were making quite an effective job of it. Their chief sent a small party to intercept us and place us under "protective arrest" for our own safety. But the real reason was that he had quite a number of casualties collected together in a small cave—a horrible place with water seeping down the walls and as cold and musty as a tomb. So I have made my first bow as a military surgeon. I did what I could for the poor devils, but it was little more than patching and plumbing; and the chances anyway were that if the Japs won the fight these casualties would be abandoned by their comrades and left for the Japanese to butcher—which is a rather nasty habit they have, though one has to remember that this is the Far East, and the Chinese are little better in their attitude to these things. The men know this and don't worry; they say it is just part of guerilla warfare.

'These poor devils were luckier than some, for actually the guerillas cleared the road and sent the Japs scurrying back in the direction of Manchukuo. I won't tell you what happened to the Jap casualties, but I expect you can guess.

'When it was all over, the Communist chief sent for me and told me, in the foul local dialect which I am only just beginning to understand clearly, that I must go back to my station and that he couldn't permit me to continue my journey—he could not have the responsibility for foreigners on his hands. Rather more to the point— I think he saw I was going to argue it out with him—he told me that the village I had intended to visit, to do what I could for a cholera outbreak, had been attacked by the Japanese and been burnt to the ground. When I expressed my horror at this news, he shrugged philosophically. "In war," he said, "these things are ordained." "But", I said, "China is not at war officially."

'He shrugged again. "The so-called Central Government does not represent the people of China," he replied. "It is we, who are the chosen instrument of the people of China, who are fighting for our land against the invaders. As for the village," he went on, "it was a very poor one. When its menfolk fled, that meant that more than thirty new combatants joined our ranks. With their flames, the Japs are adding daily to our armies."

'I had no alternative but to return. The chief thanked me elaborately for what I had done, but declined to provide me with any kind of escort. He told me I should be safer without one. If the Japs saw any of his men with us they would fire and we should be captured. If we were alone we could argue with them. I didn't like it, but he may have been right.

'It was on the way back', the letter—which was a long one, the longest I had had for some time—went on, 'that I had a striking illustration of his dictum that the Central Government did not represent the people of China and was even opposed (that was what he had implied) to the Communists. A section of the force that had repelled the

Japs was moving along on a track parallel to ours. I wished it were further, for I thought there might be danger in its proximity, but there was no other practicable route open to them or us. About a day after we had started our return journey I had heard firing and saw the guerillas preparing to defend themselves. There weren't many of them—perhaps twenty—and suddenly they were literally overborne by a force of about ten times that number. But these weren't Japs; they were soldiers of the Central Government. Shortly afterwards, their O.C. sent a guard to "collect" me and my party.

'Through all his exquisite politeness, I could see that he was in a bad temper as though he was thoroughly displeased with me. "The inscrutable Chinese" is inscrutable only to those who have not learnt his peculiar methods of emotional expression, which are as unique to him as his language.

'He asked me to give a full account of what I was doing and so on, and I did so. Unfortunately I said quite a lot about what I had been able to do for the wounded guerillas. Despite the attack on the latter, I believed that these Chinese would be glad at the news of a Jap defeat and that their hostility to the guerillas was probably a mistake. But it was entirely the wrong thing to do. He dropped all his mask and almost growled at me, telling me that I must not venture so far away into the country, but remain at the station until, like every other foreign institution, it was swept out of the country, and he commanded that I must never in any circumstances give aid to guerillas— they were outlaws in rebellion against the Central Government, and there was no war yet with Japan. A foreigner helping bandits and brigands might find himself in a very unenviable position. I felt he could hardly restrain himself from spitting when he mentioned the word "foreign" or "foreigner". It was my first glimpse of the attitude of the fanatics of the Kuomintang. . . .

'On my way out I had further evidence of the hatred the Central Government bore the Communists, who, at any rate, were doing something to stop the Japs from filching the country. Just as I had been about to leave the presence of the O.C., there had been a fusillade, of which I had taken little notice. One grows used to firing in this part of the world. This was not a guerilla attack, however. I had to thread my way through six freshly shot bodies, almost on the doorstep of the O.C.'s headquarters. They were guerillas, who had had to pay the price of taking up arms to defend their country against the Japanese invaders. I feel almost inclined to embrace the Communist cause out here. . . .'

There spoke the authentic Giovanni, the man whose normally equable temperament seethed at the sight of oppression, injustice, and brutality. The young man who had gone to the rescue of an aged professor still lived in the older, superficially changed medical missionary. And Lydia? Naturally he reported on her reactions:

'Lydia was as shocked as I had been at this affair. Out here, away from all the restrictions and obligations that life in Europe imposes, one gets a chance to express oneself, and I realized how much she must have suffered during those years when she was forced through filial duty to subjugate herself to the Fascists . . . Her hatred of tyranny is intense. You know, I believe you have a good many false ideas about her, George, one of them being that she is a rather useless creature. It will surprise you, then, to learn that she is very busy training as a nurse, and already she is a very useful addition to our strength on the station. Yes, that will astonish you, but it is no more than I expected of her. That may sound rather unappreciative, but it is not so, for, you see, I expect nothing but the finest and best from Lydia, and she never disappoints me. . . .'

Certainly the news about Lydia surprised me, though it did not inspire the admiration I think it was intended to do. Giovanni would not have liked the question that rose in my mind, for I could not help asking myself what game she was playing now and what profit there was in it.

Lydia, the 'beautiful flower of Fascism', as I had once seen her described in a newspaper, must have undergone a very sudden conversion to exhibit now an abhorrence of tyranny that led her to sympathize with Communists. And Lydia as a self-sacrificing nurse, working among unwashed and verminous Chinese peasants in an atmosphere of stenches, was almost beyond the power of imagination to portray. Perhaps, of course, I was the antithesis of Giovanni in this matter. He admitted that he expected from her 'nothing but the finest and best', while I, on the contrary, looked ever below the surface for the least worthy and most self-seeking of motives in her. A man more often than not finds what he expects to find in people so that he can always justify what he calls his judgment and others his bias to himself—pride must be served. Whether truth lay with his view or mine—or, more probably, lay between the two extremes—time and further information alone could reveal; and Giovanni's correspondence, fortified later by his diaries, was to provide all manner of indirect data, which perhaps are better interpreted by a neutral mind than by me, for from now on there will be little opportunity for comment. Giovanni's news came thick, if not fast, and it is better it should speak for itself.

Chapter Fifteen

GUERILLA SURGEON

Events moved fast in China. Japan, not satisfied that her conquest of Manchuria had convinced the Chinese of the necessity of 'docility', was now obviously going to seize both Jehol and Chahar; but even so she did not wish to indulge in open aggression. The expeditions against these provinces were, indeed, officially described as actions of the newly created government of Manchukuo and so could be dismissed as internal affairs. The League of Nations might be weak, but Japan was not yet ready to stand branded before the whole world as an open aggressor.

The news from Jehol filled me with anxiety for Giovanni; but in due course his letters came and gave his own personal reactions to the scene:

'It is open war now,' he wrote in 1933. 'The Japs are moving into the province as part of a planned military operation—though, as I dare say you have seen in your newspapers, the affair is nominally an operation by the new government of Manchukuo to restore order on its frontiers. One has to admire the Japs for their astuteness in the handling of this business whatever else one may think of them.

'Naturally, this has presented us with grave problems. It seems utterly impossible now to develop the station on anything like the lines I hoped, and indeed it is doubtful if it will be possible to keep it open much longer. A representative from H.Q. has been here—he flew here all the way from U.S., and on the way his 'plane was sniped at by Nationalist, Communist, and Jap troops alike, which shows the unenviable position we are in—and he is still here discussing the situation and what we are to do. I don't want to have to give up almost before I have started if there is any other way out. . . . Lydia, of course, is magnificent. I don't know how I could get on without her. . . .'

It was only a short letter, obviously written in haste to let me know that he was still safe, at any rate; and it was followed, after an unusually short interval, by another:

'This is to keep you up to date as far as I am able. It means a great deal to me and to Lydia, too, to know that we have a firm link with Europe still, for this world out here gets madder and madder every day. The decision has been made—at any rate officially. The station is to close at once, and the supplies and whatever we can move are to be flown into southern China, where I have had the offer of another station to run on my own. It was a tempting offer, but luckily I did not decide at once, since I felt I ought to make no decision until I had talked it over with Lydia. She might, I thought, prefer to get out of China, especially as I was told that I could have a job in America if I wished to.

'Lydia has a clear mind and has summed up the situation admirably, as it seems to me. She said that there was little prospect of doing anything worth while in southern China. I should just be one of many there and we should be stuck for a long, long time with nothing opening up before us. And she did not like the idea of America either; she felt—and it pleased me to hear her say it—that after coming so far we ought not to run away at the first sign of trouble. Then she revealed that, unbeknown to me, she had been doing a little negotiating on her own.

'A little while ago, it seems, she had met one of the chief commanders of the Communist forces up here, a man, so she says, in the personal confidence of Mao Tse-tung himself. (He is, as you probably know, the great Communist leader of China.) She told me he had made a certain suggestion to her and asked me to discuss it

M 177

with him. It was all rather mysterious, but I knew Lydia would act only in our best interests and so I allowed myself to go along to see this General Tsin. Every person of any importance in China, by the way, seems to be a general.

'Tsin turned out to be one of the newer type of Chinese—educated in America and England, but without becoming so completely Westernized that he has forgotten China. He talked to me in French, which was quite nice to hear after all this time—which reminds me that I don't think I have told you that most of the conversation at the station takes place in English, though our one English member insists that it is American. His argument was interesting. He said it was almost inevitable that Japan must quickly occupy Jehol and Chahar and perhaps push on even further. The Central Government had withdrawn all its troops from the Northeast Provinces to the south, and he doubted the sincerity of their professions that they would fight the Japanese when they were strong enough to do so and international opinion had been mobilized on China's side, for, he told me, when students in the south demonstrated against the Japs, they were violently suppressed—which I had heard from other sources. Then he went on to say that the Japs would throw us out of Jehol if we stayed, and he didn't care to prophesy what might happen in the south. His contention was that the Communists, though Chiang Kai-shek and the Kuomintang had forced them underground, were due to rise spectacularly and control all China, for the people were uniting against Japan's invasion and the Communists were the only ones showing fight. It all sounded very lucid and inevitable the way he put it, but I am not a politician. What weighed heavily with me was that Lydia, who has had far more experience of politics than I have, said she was in agreement with his view of the situation.

'Well, in the end he made me an offer to become attached to the partisans, as these Communists call their forces, as their medical officer—a sort of surgeon-general or something of that sort. He said it would be hard and dangerous, but they needed someone of the kind. I will say this for him: he made no attempt to disguise the risks but rather tended to emphasize them, for he said that, if I lined up with the Reds, I should immediately forfeit all right to any protection the Central Government might ever be able to give me, the Japs would at once be my enemies and take no regard for my foreign status, and my own government would probably conveniently forget my existence. The last didn't worry me. I imagine the Italian Government of today has no interest in me whatsoever.

'I admit it appealed to me, and I asked for time to think it over. He said I must not take more than twenty-four hours, to which I replied that it could not be, for my own people wanted my decision by the next day. That evening I made up my mind. It was already nearly made up, and it was Lydia's very cogent arguments that turned the balance finally. I agreed to become a surgeon attached to the Communist guerillas. There was a bit of a fuss with Finlay, the man who had flown over from America. He told me it was suicide and that I ought to have more regard for my wife; but Lydia was with me and soon put paid to that argument. But in the end he took the view that a fool should be allowed to hang himself in whatever way he chooses. I am quite content to let him think that if he wishes to; I don't suppose I shall ever see him again.

'I can well imagine that this news will astonish you and even lead you to share Finlay's opinions of me. But there is something more in this than lies on the surface—believe that. I have heard too much of what the Japs are doing, and I've even seen something of it, not to want to do what I can to help in their defeat, if that is possible; and if the Communists, as seems likely, are the ones who are going to do the work, then I will throw in my lot with them. That doesn't mean I've necessarily accepted their politics. I'm not sufficiently interested in politics to embrace any party.

'What is happening in the Jap-occupied territories is too ghastly to put down. Arson, pillage, and rape have been let loose in their worst possible forms. The Japanese seem to specialize in rape. Whenever they enter a Chinese village, they round up the women for a sort of mass sacrifice. The most horrible thing about it is that they seem to derive more satisfaction from the cruelties they inflict than from the actual act. Their aim is to degrade and befoul everything Chinese they can lay their hands on—apart from the few who are ready to co-operate with them on terms of slavery—and they think that by inflicting every kind of bestial treatment on women they can best show their superiority to the Chinese. It is difficult to explain. But all that and the authentic accounts of the tortures and destruction that come in have shown me that the only decent course is to do everything and anything to help those who are putting up some sort of resistance to these fiends. . . .'

Thus, in 1933, Giovanni was giving me the first glimpse of atrocities which were later to be multiplied on a vast scale throughout a great part of Asia and cause the Japanese to become regarded as almost a sub-human species. But at the time I don't think this aspect struck me so forcibly as the curious change that had again come over Giovanni's affairs. Giovanni had gone out in the first place as one who felt he had a mission of healing to perform; that was the fundamental man. But once again, as in Florence, his humanitarian instincts had been diverted and he found himself roused to militancy. Not only was he attaching himself to a fighting force, swearing, in effect, 'death to the Japs', but he was allying himself with an irregular army, illegal in the eyes of the recognized Chinese Government. As for Lydia, her conduct was becoming more and more inexplicable, on the information I had available. In the same letter he wrote of her:

'Lydia, of course, is coming with me. I did suggest she should leave China or at any rate move out of the danger area, but she just laughed, saying it was her idea in the first place and she was going to see it through. She is coming with me as aide, orderly, and nurse—and she is fully qualified for all those duties now. She can also drive a car, of course, if we can find one, and, more important still, some petrol for it.

'She is more excited about all this than I am—she says it will be the first time in her life that she has had an opportunity to do a useful job. The thought of danger doesn't influence her at all—I have never known a woman with so much courage. General Tsin seems overawed by her and is asking her advice on all sorts of matters. . . .'

His praise of Lydia continued, but need not be repeated. Towards the end he grew more specific about his new duties:

'I shall nominally be attached to Army H.Q., but that, I understand, is little more than a polite fiction, for there is no real "army" and the fighting bands are constantly on the move, acting on their own, so there is no real headquarters and few people know where the commanders are at any given time. But the idea is that I shall, with what help I can gather together, move about to wherever the need is greatest. I am to have first claim on such medical supplies as the organization can get through to me. It is not a matter of organizing a medical service, for doctors are scarce in China and scarcest of all in this part of the world. Most of the missions have moved south, and those that haven't will come, of course, under Japanese domination sooner or later. We don't hope or expect to save Jehol, but we do believe we can, by our example, do something to inflame the national spirit of the Chinese and unite them against the invaders. Already I feel that these desperate and heroic guerillas have done quite a lot towards that end. . . .'

That he did not minimize the hazards of this extraordinary adventure was shown in his final sentences.

'No one can say what the future can bring forth, but I am not unduly concerned about it. There are risks and dangers of every kind, and as the Japs are concerned, probably more terrible than anything you can imagine. For all that, I am in higher spirits than I have been for a long time. This may seem strange to you, but the mere thought that I shall have Lydia to share all this with me makes my happiness complete. In her presence, neither hardship nor risk have any meaning. She is an inexhaustible well of fortitude and inspiration on which I can draw unfailingly. There is one more thing I must tell you about us, George, in all seriousness. Both of us have taken a solemn vow that neither of us will allow ourselves to be captured by the Japanese, and we have made arrangements so that, if all else fail, we can fall back upon poison. I would rather she died by my own hand than that she get into the clutches of those fiendish Japs, to whom a white woman serving with the Red armies would be a direct gift from whatever foul devil it is that they worship above reason.

'So,' he concluded, 'this might even be the last letter I shall ever write to you. Whatever happens, communications will be difficult, so even if I have time and opportunity to write it may be months before the letter gets through to you. I shall think of you and all you have done for me, and neither I nor Lydia will forget you. Of that you may rest assured. I am proposing to keep a diary—not daily, for I don't suppose it will be easy, but whenever I can— and I shall send it to you in instalments as and if I get the chance. I shall do this for two reasons. The first is that I know you will be interested to learn of the strange life I am going to lead. The second is that I believe the truth should be known about this business. That is all, my dear George. *Au revoir*. Let us hope that it is not farewell. . . .'

That letter was remarkable in another and unprecedented way. In it was an enclosure in a sealed envelope; it was a letter from Lydia.

'Giovanni has told you our news,' she wrote, 'and I expect that cynical and not very generous mind of yours— at any rate so far as I am concerned!—has already begun to look for some sinister reason for my behaviour. No, George, you could never really disguise what you thought of me, though I admit I couldn't help admiring you for your efforts to play up to Giovanni. Well, it may not matter much now, for he and I are certainly putting our necks on the chopping-block, and the chances of our coming out of this alive are not very good. Now I expect you think I am posing again and dramatizing myself as a heroine-to-be. I'm not.

'All the same, I *have* got a motive for what I have persuaded Giovanni to do, and it may surprise you to learn the real truth—which is simply that I want to see he has a chance of doing himself justice. He is quite the nicest man I have ever known, and I am really very fond of him, whatever you may think. He is the most honest, loyal, self-sacrificing man I have ever met, and sometimes he makes me feel a little mean and tawdry. But you know as well as I do, George, that men who are really honest and loyal and self-sacrificing don't go far in this hard world— they're so busy looking after other people that they forget all about themselves. That is where I come in. I am doing the thinking and planning for him. I want to see him at the top of the tree, which is where he belongs—and also the last place he would think of climbing to by himself. So there it is in a nutshell.

'I have been talking to people who ought to know— though I cannot talk to many, for so far I haven't made much progress with this infernal Chinese language—and it does seem to me, *at present*'—those italics are hers; she was a vigorous underliner—'that the Reds are the people to back. The Chinese hate the Japanese like poison, and it is the Communists who are doing all the fighting, besides which they are always talking of reorganizing the country in favour of the peasants, a bait that never fails to win support in any country. Whether they fulfil their promises or not hardly matters. The point is that they are the most likely, as things stand, to win power, and the people who get in with them now will reap the benefit. Giovanni may become Director-General of Chinese Health Services yet. If it's possible, I'll see that he will.

'Of course, these things want close watching. The wind might shift at any moment, but Giovanni is the last person in the world to keep his eyes open for things of that kind. He will probably be too absorbed by his cases to remember whether it's the Reds or the Kuomintang he is working for. But I have played this game before, not altogether unsuccessfully, and this time I shall be playing it for Giovanni rather than myself, which will make me even more alert to coming changes. If both of us survive, I am not going to see Giovanni remain as a mere field sawbones or family doctor-nurse to louse-ridden peasants in their hovels.

'I am telling you the truth, George. I wonder if you will believe it? Is it such a very unworthy motive? Don't you with your knowledge of Giovanni admit that he needs someone to push him on to the heights of which he is capable? An idea or an ideal will rouse him and he'll work like the devil for it—but never, never for himself or his own betterment. Well, now he's going to work for *me*. . . .'

Together, these two letters dazed me. The enigma of Lydia deepened with every fresh glimpse I had of her.

Chapter Sixteen

DIARIST'S DIFFICULTIES

When, at last, the first instalment of the diaries arrived, its pages proved to be even more informing than Giovanni's letters had been. For one thing, the items had been written down when they were fresh in his mind; he gave himself no time to prune them—for which reason some of them were inordinately long. For another, he was obviously a born diarist, in the sense that when he made entries he was doing so without any conscious thought of their being read at any time by anyone else; he wrote for his own eyes alone. So far, then, they were excellent material, which I perused with deep interest. Nevertheless they had grave faults. As the events described revealed, they were written under the heaviest handicaps; this meant that they alternated between unnecessary fulsomeness and sheer scrappiness. In addition they were in all manner of forms: some entries were made in school exercise books, others in expensive, leather-backed volumes that looked as though they had been prepared for some official archives, while at the other extreme were loose sheets of paper of all kinds—including wrapping paper—which were not always arranged in the correct order. To add to this last-named difficulty, some of the items were not even dated, while the handwriting often bordered on the illegible. Deciphering certain pages took an immense amount of time, which I could ill spare. I do not say that all these advantages and disadvantages, the good qualities and the bad, were apparent from the start; they could not be. What I have written of them is the result of a series that covered several years, and I have tried to sum it up before giving essential extracts.

Before taking up the story of Giovanni's life with the guerillas—his first entry into warfare—it may perhaps be wise to give, from entries in the diaries at various periods, indications of the difficulties under which they were compiled. This will serve to forestall any criticisms that experts, working in the armchairs in their studies, may feel inclined to make on the score of accuracy or misdescription. These writings were not scholarly evaluations but the actual, living reactions of a sensitive mind to daily experience, a mind that could not see the picture whole, but was deeply concerned with one small individual piece of it. These hints at problems of compilation run throughout the whole of the lengthy series and can be picked out almost at random.

Here, for example, is one from some period in 1934—it cannot be dated more exactly than that:

'In this place one suffers from the monotony of variety, if one can use such a phrase. No two days are alike, and so one loses all sense of direction or sequence in life. There are no marks to which to refer time, and one loses one's way in the calendar. For some time past I have not known what day of the week it is, far less the day of the month, though I do know it is 1934 and somewhere in mid summer. The Chinese, who seem to keep their calendars in their heads, will tell me that it is the nth moon, but that information is useless because I have no data to convert it into our system. . . .'

And again, of the problems of obtaining writing materials:

'I did not expect to be able to resume this diary so soon, for when I had finished my previous entry a couple of days ago I had used my last piece of paper and been forced to squeeze the last half-dozen lines into an uncomfortably small space. But this morning, thank God, we had some fresh medical supplies brought up to us, and some of the items were packed in pure white wrapping paper, the sight of which, its potentialities as writing material, made my mouth water. It has a somewhat glazed surface which is not too kind to the pen, but it is all the same a real godsend.' (Here there was a large blot.) 'That untidy blot shows the sort of surface it is—the ink runs over it instead of being slightly absorbed as it should be. As I am now forced to use the stick-ink of the Chinese, this difficulty is even greater than it would be if I could use my favourite fountain-pen, which has been such a good friend to me since my student days. . . .'

Other practical handicaps had to be overcome by the diarist:

'One of the most curious difficulties I have to face in writing this diary is that of light. By day I am too busy and preoccupied to do any writing, and at night there is practically no illumination at all. Paraffin is scarce and has to be kept for really essential purposes, so our life is like that of the Chinese peasants among whom we work and live—when the sun goes down, the day is over and there is nothing to do but go to bed. Even though today I am enjoying the luxury of a few hours' rest while a new convoy is assembled for the next trip, I am still faced with the difficulty of light. The rains are here, and one does not go outdoors unless it is essential; certainly one could not use pen and ink in that Niagara which is pouring down from the heavens. (The Chinese are talking of floods again; they are never free from one or other of their three curses: flood, famine, and epidemic.) It is not much better in this hut, for the roof leaks and the water is running down the walls. As for light, there are two squares of oiled paper, each perhaps three hundred millimetres square, which, so far from being sources of illumination, give me the impression merely of dyeing the gloom a deep yellow. But I am managing somehow. . . .'

These are typical specimens selected almost at random from the many that could have been used. Time and again he returns to the problems of writing, for compilation of his diary seems to have become almost an obsession with him. Apart from his work and his care for Lydia, which transcended all else, he gives the impression that he would forgo a good many things rather than writing materials. If there were pens, there was no ink; if he had both pen and ink, paper was scarce. He improvised. There are several sheets written—or scrawled, which is the better description—on coarse kraft paper in some sort of red pigment, giving to the whole the air of some fantastic survival of a prehistoric age. Perhaps it was to these sheets that he referred when he made this comment:

'My last pen having broken, I have been trying to use the small brush that the Chinese employ for their writing. My efforts have not been very successful, though they are more legible than I might have expected. The brush, too, is a better implement to use when the only paper is the heavy coarse stuff that is used for parcels. On this an ordinary pen-nib is useless; it takes up the innumerable loose fibres from the surface. . . .'

Experience of scarcity increases the joy of possession when the latter is realized, however imperfectly, as this item shows:

'Stores again today. I was down to my last field dressing, and I had been treasuring my last drop of morphine as a rich blessing only for one whose agony was beyond endurance. How often have I wished for more of that blessed alkaloid when I have seen human beings writhing with a pain to which even death must have seemed infinitely preferable! But it was not only medical supplies. There was paper and some note-books—above all, some pencils! Six of them, with bright yellow enamel surfaces that remind me of the daffodils in Spring at home. I have laid them out on the small bench in front of me, treasures beyond the price of diamonds and rubies. These are things for which I have longed—yet shall I have the courage ever to sharpen them and use them? I shall know that with each word I write the precious point is reduced by a little and that after a while I must resharpen the pencil. So it will go on till my treasure is exhausted, broken down into the dust of wood and graphite. And I cannot help wondering if anything I can write can possibly be one half—one quarter, even—as precious as those beautiful and entrancing pencils. . . .'

There is a curious echo in that last sentence of two famous lines in the Rubaiyat of Omar Khayyam, but I doubt whether Giovanni, whose upbringing and education had been entirely Italian, and who, at that, was far from literary minded, had ever heard of them.

Shortage close to famine was the keynote in everything, the *leitmotif* of his daily round. One way round was ingenuity and turning articles at hand to unintended purposes—though sometimes this led to unexpected results. For instance:

'Once more I have come to the end of my paper for the time being. There is not a scrap of paper of any kind or cardboard anywhere, though we have searched high and low. Lydia suggested that we should try stripping the covers off some old textbooks I have been carting round with me and using the material to write upon after we had washed out the dye. I fell in with the idea, for the books are useless and I think by now I know them word by word by heart. We tried the experiment, which, in itself, was highly successful, for we found we have several sizeable pieces of close fabric like linen. But that is far too valuable to use for writing. It will make admirable dressings for small wounds and I have put it carefully into my fast dwindling store. . . .'

I doubt whether any medical publisher ever thought that his productions would be put to such supremely practical use as this.

These extracts have been given as a prelude to the more autobiographical details to indicate the conditions under which the diaries were written. Yet they are not without their value as indices to Giovanni's complex character and the attitude he had begun to adopt as part of his normal self. He had become in his own mind an integral part of the Chinese scene and could imagine nothing else. He can mention the 'daffodils at home' with no hint of nostalgia, but merely as a passing thought of no great importance to him. Shortages and make-shifts, hardships and discomfort—all these are things not to be merely endured but taken as the norm of life. He does not seem at any stage—nor does Lydia, with her shrewdness appear to have reminded him—that, after all, he was a European who had no need to be there sharing these tribulations with the Chinese. At any time he could have broken free, demanded escort back to a safe area, and then gone almost where he would to places in which he could have lived the life of a highly skilled doctor.

One of Giovanni's strongest traits was his power of dedication—there is no other word for it. He did not merely accept employment or set up an ambition before himself; if he took up anything he gave himself wholly to it. I myself am inclined to believe that, even without Lydia's strange prompting, he would, in the circumstances that had arisen, still thrown in his lot with the Chinese. Lydia might profess to see in all this merely a means to an end and hold the view that this privation was merely a temporary price to pay in the cause of ultimate advancement. I hesitate to think that such a thing ever occurred to Giovanni. He was with the Chinese guerillas. So far as a European might, he was one of them. He would have considered it outrageous that he should not have led the same life as they did or that he should have been accorded any special privileges. Lydia had indeed spoken the truth when she had said that he was so busy thinking of other people that he had no time to think of himself.

Chapter Seventeen

INITIAL PROBLEMS

The diaries reveal that it did not take long for Giovanni to realize that he had to face problems even greater than he had expected. An early entry runs:

'Tsin has formally invested me with the local command of all medical services, which sounds very imposing. He has told me what I expected, that medical supplies are scarce and that the difficulties of transport even when they are available is great, and so a great deal of improvisation will be required. That again is what I expected. Allowing for all that, however, conditions are worse than I anticipated, perhaps insuperable in some aspects.

'This business of my being "in local command" is ironically amusing. It is very much like being an admiral in the Swiss Navy, for there is literally nothing to command. For the past two days I have been working with a minimum of sleep to try and get some idea of the general position. I find that the medical services of which I am to take charge don't exist—nor is there much out of which to create them. I am the only European doctor working in this sector. In the next, which may be two hundred miles away or five—no one knows in this strange business of here today and gone tomorrow—they are very proud of the fact that they have two doctors. Both are Chinese and graduated in the United States. Very few of the actual guerillas have any knowledge of first aid, so that, as I have already learnt, by the time I or anyone else can get to the worst cases, they are practically beyond help. But there are difficulties of other kinds, perhaps more baffling than the practical ones, which in all conscience could hardly be worse.

'First of all, there are the dozen or so "medical orderlies" as they call them who, up to now, have run the so-called casualty services on their own. They are Chinese who have picked up some sort of knowledge of first-aid either at the missions or in one of the coast towns. They resent my presence. In the first place, my arrival may probably cause them some loss of face, which is a very serious matter for them (far more important than that my presence may help to save a few more valuable lives); it will be a hard task to win their co-operation. In the second place, they do not like me because I am a foreigner and a European at that. Their attitude is that they are fighting to get rid of foreign influence in China and want China to belong to the people—the peasants—and they should, as a matter of principle, do nothing to suggest that Europeans are in any way better than they are themselves. It is no good to point out to them that I am just a doctor with no political or commercial axe to grind, or even that I am an Italian whose country has had nothing to do with the more flagrant exploitation of China, the blame for which must rest on the shoulders of the British, Americans, and French, principally. All Europeans are the same to them, and I am a European. Only fear from Tsin and his authority, which is very firmly exercised, enables me to be tolerated at all so far.

'Then there are the patients themselves. When a Chinese peasant leaves his plot to become a guerilla—either because he feels impelled to or because the Japs or the Kuomintang or the local war lords and their clique have dispossessed him—he still remains a Chinese peasant. The gun in his hand does not change his mentality. He still believes in his traditional "cures" and it will be hopeless, I think, to try to raise the health level and reduce the casualty rate by endeavouring to pump a few elementary facts of hygiene and first-aid into these men.

Their minds are utterly closed and barred against it. I can't see that there would ever be time on this job to go in for statistical research, even if the data could be obtained, but I should be very interested to find out just how much the overall death rate from casualties has been increased by Chinese medicine, which, so far as I can make out, relies principally on dung, human hair, nail parings, and the most evil-smelling and foul tasting herbs and plants, for everything from an emetic to a wound dressing.

'It is useless to point out that by doing so-and-so one can save life. Life has little value to them in the Western sense. Death is nothing to be afraid of and can be a very happy release from present suffering. Moreover, it is usually the spirits who have the last say in matters of life and death, so why make the question unduly complicated? All this goes oddly with the Communist slogans and Marxian arguments they have learnt (parrot-wise, I fear, in most cases) and that they use them almost as charms and incantations.

'This, of course, reacts on the problem of medical supplies, which is difficult enough as it is. Men engaged on convoy work regard the medical supplies as the least important of all. If some of them die *en route* or are killed, or rivers are swollen and difficult to cross, it is the medical packages that get abandoned first. The order of precedence is ammunition, clothing, food, medical supplies. Their argument is that ammunition must be got through; they can't make it themselves. Clothing can be improvised but is better obtained ready made. Food can be picked up everywhere, for it takes a great deal to shift the Chinese peasant from his plot and he will carry on his work even in the middle of a pitched battle. As for medical supplies— why worry about them at all? Men still die whether they are there or not; and the aforesaid dung, etc., is available in quantity on the spot, so why not use that as their forefathers have for generations?. . .'

Administrative problems, however, were not allowed to bulk too large in Giovanni's affairs. However high-sounding the titles and commands that might have been conferred on him, his principal job was to act as a field-surgeon wherever he could. Almost immediately after the entry just quoted, this occurs:

'Yesterday evening, a scout came in to report there had been quite a heavy skirmish about fifty miles away. The local guerillas have fallen on a Jap column and cut it to pieces badly, though with very considerable losses to themselves. He brought, in addition to this news, an urgent plea for more ammunition. Tsin, who is still with us, immediately ordered out a column and told me I had better go along with it to see if I could do anything. It was my first real assignment as an "army" doctor.

'The route was hard going, especially as we travelled the first stages by night. The Chinese think nothing of these things, but it was very trying and indeed painful for us. Lydia, of course, had insisted on coming with me. I think our stock slumped even lower in the estimation of the men. We are an embarrassment that they would much rather lose, were it not for the certainty of Tsin's anger if we failed to return, and furthermore no fewer than three porters were engaged in carrying our medical supplies, which they looked on as superfluous. I had tried to get hold of more, but it was hinted by the captain of the column that there might well be mutiny if I insisted too much.

'The journey took us about forty hours, with the briefest of halts for food and rest. Assuming that the messenger had taken only half as long as that to bring us the news, it meant that the casualties must have lain at least sixty hours without attention so I was prepared for the worst. I did not anticipate being able to do much.

'It was a pretty terrible sight when at last I got to it. I don't know whether the place—a kind of broken-down hovel—was meant to be a dressing-station, a field hospital, or a morgue. It looked more like the last to me. I never expected to see as much gangrene in one place at one time as there was there; and practically all of it was quite beyond my aid, even had I better facilities than I had. The living, the just-living, and the dead, both recent and less recent, were all muddled together in an atmosphere of stench and flies. No one seemed to care particularly. There were men who had bled to death unnecessarily for it was quite obvious that an immediate application of a field-dressing would almost certainly have saved them. In my innocence I took it for granted that this was due to there being no field dressings.

'I was disillusioned quite soon, for I found an unopened pack of them—about fifty—in a corner of that very shed. This made me lose my temper and I sought out the O.C. and expressed myself with rather more vigour than is usual in China. I paid little attention to the polite formulae one is supposed to employ. The O.C. was quite unperturbed. He just shrugged his shoulders and said it was quite useless to issue field dressings to each man, as is done in European armies. The men would use them for anything and everything except their proper purpose, so it was better to keep them in a sealed box where they would not get wasted. . . .'

The shock of this first ghastly impression of a guerilla casualty station was not, however, without a practical lesson to teach Giovanni. He had seen something which cried out for correction; he forgot his indignation and disgust in trying to turn his experience to good account. After some further details, he continued:

'If I have been able to do little today to save lives, at least I have learnt a lot. The next step is to see how this chaos and criminality can be cleared up. . . .'

In the next entry he developed this theme:

'In the two days since I returned from the shambles I have spent most of my time thinking about what I saw and how to rectify it. Tsin is not very helpful, though he says that conditions in his sectors are probably worse than elsewhere. In other places, it seems, the guerillas have attached to them considerable numbers of students from the Chinese universities, which have been among the strongest centres of Communism, and they form the nucleus of a reasonable emergency medical service. Most of them, I understand, are refugees, not from the Japs but from the Kuomintang, which has been specially oppressive to any sign of Communism in the universities. He insists that I am the only one with any real medical knowledge and experience in his command—no wonder he was so keen to get hold of me! But that is beside the point. The key to my problem seems to lie in that package of unused field dressings—which, incidentally, I brought away with me as a welcome addition to my exiguous supplies. I shall tackle the "medical orderlies", despite all their opposition, and try to secure some more volunteers. Even if I have to use a whip, I shall drive it into their heads that their job is to do everything they can to save lives, which are, at the lowest, valuable to the guerillas. I shall attach at least one of these men, when I have trained them, to each of the individual fighting units in Tsin's command, and he will have charge of the supplies and be responsible under the direst penalty—his life if necessary; I can get Tsin to agree to that—for seeing that they are used properly. Even a Chinese can probably be stirred to save someone else's life if he feels that his own is in danger! Lydia agreed with this course when I talked it over with her. She believes that the only way to handle these people is to be utterly ruthless with them—and so, if that is the right way, I intend to be. . . .'

Giovanni had little opportunity of putting his proposed ruthlessness—a strange policy for him—into effect, at all events in the way he proposed. Four days later he was on the trail again, summoned to attend to the casualties of another Japanese-guerilla encounter about half a day's journey away. This time he was prepared for what he was to see—in some respects at least:

'Conditions here were a little better, probably because there had not been time enough for them to get worse. There were, too, a couple of "medical orderlies" on the spot, and rather to my surprise they turned out to be keen and intelligent fellows, though some of their bandaging would have been a disgrace to a Boy Scouts' first-aid party. The casualties themselves were not so severe. It is true that the same unlovely stench overhung everything, but the Chinese do not seem to notice it, and the curious thing is that it doesn't seem to affect them at all adversely. Animal powers of adaptation are quite remarkable. Lydia again came with me—I think by a deliberate effort of will. The earlier sights had upset her but not unnerved her, and now that she has proved herself she is anxious to habituate herself to conditions so that she can be of the greatest help to me.

'Outside the hut that served as the casualty station, I found a body covered with a filthy cloth, from beneath which were coming groans of a very distressing kind. To my astonishment, the "medical orderly" with me took no notice; he might not have heard the groans for all the signs he gave.

'I examined the casualty, who turned out to be a rather puzzling case. All his toes were dislocated, as were his thumbs, and there was extensive bruising and damage across his back as though he had been unmercifully flogged.

'I told the orderly to take him into the hospital. He did not move. He told me the man was a Japanese officer who had been captured and so it did not matter. "He is in serious pain," I said. "Obey my orders." The orderly looked at me. "He is a Jap," he replied. I was furious. Jap or not, the man was in a bad state and something had to be done for him. I strode over to the O.C. who was a little way off and asked for his help and explanation. He was even more unperturbed than the orderly.

' "If he is in pain," he said to me, "that is all to the good. It shows that we know our job. He would not talk, so he had to be encouraged." I asked him, almost unable to believe it, if it was torture. He seemed astonished that I should ask such a question, and admitted it without a tremor. It was not something I could protest about, but I did ask him to order the orderly to carry him into the hospital and help me to make him comfortable. "But why?" asked the O.C. as though I was a stupid child. "He is Japanese and we do not want him to get well. What should we do with a Japanese on our hands? He has told us all he knows so he is no more use to us." I insisted that, as a doctor, it did not matter to me whether he was Chinese, Japanese, or what; my job was to save life. "Chinese lives," he said. "Communist Chinese lives. That is all."

'It is difficult for me to get this perspective in which lives have definite values. But it was useless to argue. I should get no help from anyone; and when I returned to the Jap and re-examined him and tried to make him comfortable, I could feel that I was taking a considerable risk with my standing, such as it was, among the guerillas. The officers in particular were hard put to it to hide their disgust and rage. He was worse than I had thought. From the blood he was spitting up I suspected serious internal injuries, probably as the result of his beatings, but it was impossible to do much for him. The best I could do was to give him a shot of my precious morphine and hope that his last dreams would not be too troubled by the crimes and atrocities he had no doubt committed and those that had been inflicted on him by others. . . .'

This education into the peculiar requirements of military surgery among the guerillas went on apace. A few weeks later, we find Giovanni taking all the horrors for granted, dismissing wounded or tortured Japs, who had been unfortunate enough to survive in Chinese hands, with mere alleviative measures and accepting as a high recovery rate one in twenty cases treated. Yet he was not at ease in his mind, as this entry, some time after the events just recorded, shows:

'I had to leave another poor Jap to die today. It has to be done if I am not to run the risk of torture and death myself, but I hate doing it. A life is a life, whomever it may belong to, and it is really my duty to attempt to save it no matter what the opposition may be. I have taken an opportunity of discussing this aspect with Lydia, and rather to my surprise I find her not at all unsympathetic to the Chinese viewpoint. She says that war is war, and all of it is terrible but this is more terrible than most. Chinese prisoners have not a chance in Jap hands, she said, and so why should Japs be more favourably treated? Besides, she went on, guerillas moving about the country have no facilities for keeping prisoners, and if they allow me to save the lives of Japs and then have to turn them loose, it only means that I shall be helping the enemy. I have no doubt that all this is very realistic, and it is very like Lydia to put all her natural womanhood aside and present this unsympathetic view to me, but all the same the mere idea of it makes me shudder. But war, as she says, is a terrible business, and this is not so much a war as organized brigandage and murder. . . .'

Shortly after this, Giovanni's mood changed to one of expectation and pleasure. Tsin had visited the encampment again and told him that he had been lucky enough to secure another European doctor to assist him.

'This is good news,' he wrote in his diary. 'Tsin does not seem to know much about the man, but whoever he is I shall be more than glad to have some sort of skilled assistance in this place and someone with whom I can discuss the problems in a rational way. At times I've felt that I am the only sane person among the released personnel of a lunatic asylum. I believe that feeling is sometimes taken as proof of madness in the person who says it, but that can apply only to Europe not to China. He is due here in about a week. . . .'

Yet it was a fortnight before the new doctor was to arrive. There had been trouble along the route, and the convoy had had to make a wide detour as well as engage in a minor skirmish. And when he did come, Giovanni did not seem at all pleased with his first impressions:

'The promised new man has arrived, and he turns out to be a *very* young Englishman named Leopold Colson, but he insists on being called, for some reason which he will not or cannot explain, "Butts". These English and their confounded nicknames! He is an ardent Communist. I don't know whether they turn people out of England for being rabid revolutionaries of that kind, but if so, that explains his presence here. He is properly qualified, but that is about all. His experience, I imagine, is practically nothing, so it looks as though I shall have a student to train as well as my other troubles. Perhaps I should have been better without him after all. Like all young men, and Englishmen in particular, he is quite convinced that he knows everything and that the things he has read in the latest textbooks are far more important than what I have learnt through hard experience. Even if I haven't time, China should teach him a lot. . . .'

First impressions are often revised. Giovanni quickly altered his. An entry about six weeks later runs:

'A hard day, if ever there was one. At work at dawn and at it steadily all day till nightfall, when the lack of oil and candles forced us to stop. Butts, as usual, has been magnificent. I can't imagine how I ever got on without him. He is absolutely tireless and is sufficiently English to forget his Communism at times and become really dictatorial with the "damned Chinese" as he calls them to get what he wants. Lydia likes him, and I am glad she has company. His Italian is foul and he thinks my American-English little better, but he is picking up Chinese rapidly. I think, too, he has the makings of a good doctor in him. Meantime he takes a great weight off my shoulders. . . .'

Chapter Eighteen

RETREAT TO THE SOUTH

In pressing Giovanni to join the Communist guerillas and accepting for herself the hardships that that act entailed, Lydia was taking a very long chance indeed on the future eminence she professed to see for her husband. Political events were moving swiftly in China and their impact on his own immediate affairs were to provide further problems for Giovanni.

The year 1933 was drawing to its close, and the Communist guerillas were still waging their desperate, ingenious and brilliantly courageous war against the Japanese. But it was no more than a nuisance to the Japs; it lacked any real central strategy or overall plan, and if it had possessed such a thing, its forces would have been totally inadequate. Step by step, hotly disputed mile by mile, the Reds were yielding control of the provinces of Jehol and Chahar which the Central Government had earlier deserted to their fate. The stern march of events was at last beginning to impress itself on Giovanni:

'I have been enjoying an unexpected luxury,' he confided to his diary. 'For two whole days I have been doing nothing. For some time now I have not been well, though there has been nothing wrong with me to which one could put a name—just general lassitude and fatigue due, I suppose, to too much work and too little rest in this far from salubrious climate. "Butts", exerting his medical authority (!), has insisted that I shall rest. Whatever else this may or may not have done for me it has given me time for reflection—something I have not had for a very long time, and I have been trying to put the thing into its place. I have been too close up to one small sector of these events to have any idea of what has been happening over the whole field. Guerilla warfare is notoriously difficult to follow, for there is no set front and not even, in the true sense, a theatre of operations. Scattered forces turn up at all sorts of unexpected places and do their work—that is the fundamental of the whole technique. The Jap lines may be here in one place, but the partisans are just as likely to make a sudden foray north, south, east, or west of it.

'I have talked to Butts about this, as well as to other people, including Tsin; and everyone seems to take rather a gloomy outlook. Something is happening that does not presage at all well for the guerilla war. It is beginning to take a recognizable pattern, and if once it gets set it is to all intents and purposes over. Every action reported is a little further south of the previous one. More than that, more than ninety per cent of the guerilla raids now take place on the southern side of the established Japanese advancing columns—that is on our side so to speak. Behind the Jap lines all is quiet—and that can mean only one thing: that the Japs have crushed resistance there. Further, it means added strength for the final Jap push against us. Now they know that, except for a very sporadic raid, their lines of communication are safe. In other words, the two provinces are now inevitably doomed, though that does not necessarily mean that all Chinese resistance is crushed. After all our high hopes and our considerable early successes, this is poor news indeed. Though I had sensed that all was not going so well as we wished, I had not realized before that the shape of events was so ominous . . .'

He had time, too, during this obviously much-needed rest to gather reports about what was happening in southern China.

'The more I hear about the policy of the Central Government in Nanking,' he comments, 'the less explicable it seems to me. Here in the north-east, the Chinese people have been waging an heroic resistance against invaders whose brutality, ruthlessness, lust, and greed, must surely be unequalled in history; and their power for devilry is all the worse because they have harnessed the most modern weapons of war to a primitive barbarity. The Central Government does nothing more than protest to the League of Nations at Geneva. It withdrew its forces from these provinces at the first sign of possible trouble. Yet the Kuomintang continuously asserts that it is the saviour of China and that its leader, Chiang Kai-shek, is a heaven-sent prophet of nationalism. They argue that before Japan can be fought on equal terms with any chance of success, China must be united from north to south, east to west, under their leadership. Union, at this rate, should eventually be easy, for Japan is likely to have snapped up almost the whole country before they have begun to move!

'When I think of all that these heroic guerillas have gone through for no other inducement than the future liberty of their country and its people, and compare it with the activities of the Kuomintang and Central Government, I can only wonder that the latter are not smitten dumb with shame. For they have ample resources. They are fed by American and British money and supplies; they have a large and effective army trained and to some extent officered by Germans, those masters of warfare on land, and possessing ports wide open to import what they need; they have not, in the face of this ghastly threat and the ravages done to their own motherland, been content with mere inactivity but have gone to war—not with the national enemy, the Japanese, but with the Communists, whom they have vowed to crush. At times, one is forced to the conclusion that they hate the Japanese less than the Communists, and that they would rather be crushed by the Japs than compromise with the Communists. It is strange to find a nation at civil war within itself when the foreign invader is not merely at the gates but successfully forcing his way in.

'South of the Yangtze, all the massive strength of the Central Government is directed towards hemming in the Communists with the ultimate purpose of their complete extermination and reduction. It is even safer, I am told, to be of avowed Japanese sympathies than to hold Communist connections wherever the rule of the Central Government is strong. . . .'

Nevertheless, Giovanni retained his native caution.

'Even to myself I cannot pretend that my own summing up of it is a correct and complete picture. It could hope to be neither. I have to remember, too, that the majority of my informants are connected with the Communists, and their stories, therefore, are likely to be strongly biased. . . .'

For all that, the general outline as he gave it in these airy passages was not so far from the truth, as we now know from other sources. At the time it was written, it would no doubt have appeared as strongly coloured by the Red dye, at any rate to the outside world, which was fed almost entirely on the Central Government official accounts of affairs in China.

Steadily, the guerilla forces moved southwards:

'Every day we strike camp and move a little further to the south,' noted Giovanni at the turn of the year. 'There is no particular hurry about it, and the plan seems to be to withdraw all the remaining guerillas along converging routes to a common focus, where they can be formed into a new army to be placed at the disposal of the Communist leaders for service—preferably against Japan, but in the Civil War if that is decided necessary. I feel practically unemployed now. Such fighting as does occur takes place in the most remote parts, where aid, either military or medical, could not be sent in time to be of any value.

'The Central Government might be surprised if it sent some of its representatives to these areas. The Communists have become national heroes, the defenders of China; and in every village we enter on our march south we are greeted with acclamations, as though we were glorious

204

victors. The humblest partisan is treated with the highest honours, and even the two insignificant white doctors, foreign devils though they be, are greeted with respect and sometimes even applause as participators in the fight for freedom. On one occasion, we were actually garlanded with the rest by the inhabitants of a small town! It was a remarkable experience indeed. Poor Butts was utterly embarrassed and looked as though he would bolt for shelter at any moment. But then he is English. . . ."

He gives a glimpse of Lydia at this time, a changed woman, as well she might be:

'This quiet time of reflection has given me a chance to see Lydia in a new light. She is a very different woman from the scared girl who came out here with me. Her interests have altered a good deal, and she is now a most competent nurse and orderly. When I have to perform one of my emergency operations, which are pretty grim travesties of surgery, I would rather have her at my side than Butts, for though the latter has toned down a lot he still retains a good deal of youthful bumptiousness and omniscience. She and he spend a good deal of time together, and they discuss the political situation and China's probable future at great length. I do not join in these debates. No doubt Lydia would not be the same success as she used to be in a European drawing-room, but she has developed into a fine and outstanding woman, with a look of resolution and courage rare in a woman's face, and her figure, while retaining all its feminine loveliness, has added to it the grace of a good athlete. She is an object of awe and wonder to the Chinese, for even Communism and Westernization have failed to eradicate entirely the ingrained Chinese belief that women are of necessity inferior in all things to men. If I raise my eyes and look through the open door of the tent in which I write, I can see her now, silhouetted against the setting sun—a vision that still sets my heart beating more rapidly. Butts has just passed by and called out something to her. She has laughed, as I have heard her laugh a thousand,

205

a hundred thousand times, and I fall to wondering how I could ever have gone through so much for so long without that enchanting sound, which has everything in common with the clean, tingling, exhilarating winds of the mountains. We are husband and wife; we are lovers; and perhaps even greater than that, we have between us that deep comradeship which comes only of a common experience and endurance of trials, agonies, and horrors, the mere imagination of which is, thank God, beyond the powers of most people in Europe. . . .'

Circumstances were to force his gaze before very long on aspects of humanity far less pleasing to him than Lydia. In its march south, the column was joined by another withdrawing guerilla band, and the combined forces moved on together. This was a greater concentration of strength than Giovanni had yet seen.

'The sight of so many men,' he observes, 'makes one realize on how large a scale the guerillas have been fighting, for this is still only a small fraction of the total and it looks highly impressive. Our own small unit had seemed so small and insignificant that it was difficult on occasions to imagine how the movement was managing to inflict any damage at all on the Japs. Yet these two groups together are quite a small army, and to them must be added many others which have fought over the vast areas of the north-eastern provinces. But there are many millions of human beings in China and its distances are vast, so that a European cannot always accustom himself to the scale of the business. Some say that those are the only two things in which China is rich: men and space. . . .'

Three days later, the peaceful progress of the groups was interrupted.

'Tonight,' wrote Giovanni, 'war came back to us. A dispatch runner came in with terrifying news. A third group marching in to join us had been trapped in a village where it was resting and was fighting valiantly against overwhelming odds. But this time the enemy was not the Japs. The troops of the Central Government had laid the

ambush and were fighting their fellow-countrymen with a
ferocity that made even Japanese methods seem gentle.
So the messenger said.

'Orders to march were given at once. The comrades
could not be deserted. But among officers and men alike
there was an air of weariness and repugnance quite unlike
the enthusiasm with which they would set out on the most
desperate attack on the Japs. Instinctively they were
expressing their feeling of the futility of fighting fellow
Chinese when the real enemy was the foreign invader. . . .'

They reached the village too late. The battle was over,
and the victors, the Nationalists, had left the field to the
flames and the dead:

'We could see the reflection of the flames in the sky long
before we were within even rifle-range of the village. All of
us knew it was a funeral pyre. We pressed forward hoping
that we might be able at least to extract some revenge for
the horrors we knew had been committed. There is not
much to burn in a Chinese village, which is no more than
a collection of the meanest hovels, and what there is soon
burns itself out. The fire was almost over by the time we
arrived. We were able to march in and survey the havoc.

'I do not think that I have ever seen anything grimmer
than this, though perhaps the knowledge that the evil had
been wrought not by alien but Chinese hands played a
subtle part in forming my judgment. Probably in villages
wrecked by the Japs I have collected more evidence of
actual atrocities, mutilations, rape, and the like; that I
admit. But never, I am sure, had I seen so many dead. It
had been a massacre. The Nationalists had not treated the
affair in the village as an episode of war but as an
execution.

'It had all the air of deliberation. In the village itself
were masses of bodies, civilians and guerillas alike, piled
together and charred by the flames that had so lately died
down. There were partisans still grasping their useless
weapons in their hands. There was an old woman lying
over the bucket she had obviously been carrying when a

bullet had struck her in the back of the neck. Two small children lay, smiling macabrely as their sightless eyes stared at the sky, over which the grey dawn was now spreading.

'But it was outside the village, where the flames had not reached, that the most horrible evidence of this ruthlessness was made plainest. This had obviously been an execution ground. Here we found whole families yoked together with their hands pinioned behind them—grandparents, parents, children even as young as perhaps two years. Their bodies told the tale of how they had died—they had been mowed down with machine guns.

'There did not appear to be a single survivor, and it was only when our commander had decided to withdraw and we were perhaps a mile on the road back to our camp that a partisan, his arm clumsily bandaged in a dirty rag sopping with blood, came out of cover and told us something of the story. I heard it all while I was dressing the wound. It had been a surprise attack. The troops had moved in quietly surprising even the ever-alert guerillas, and they had posted machine guns at all the exits from the village so that there was no escape. Systematically they had searched every house, dragged forth every occupant, irrespective of age or sex, and put them to death. Some were shot in the streets, others taken to the execution ground. The guerillas had fought gamely and valorously, but they had had no chance; and pitched battles against odds of this kind were not their forte. But not one surrendered. This man himself had managed to escape from a house which had been ignited over his head; his comrade had plunged a knife into his own heart.

'This was indeed a shattering experience. I was glad that on this occasion Lydia did not accompany me. It was all so senseless, so utterly insane and unjust. For those who had been massacred were guilty of no crime but that of defending their country against invasion and rapine, or, if they had been villagers, giving shelter to the men who had put up the defence. As I write these lines, the words of the medical orderly who helped me examine the massed bodies for possible survivors come back to me. He looked sadly at the holes the bullets had made—some of the unfortunate people had as many as twenty machine-gun bullets in them—and said slowly, "If only we'd had all those bullets out there", and he pointed to the north-east. Yes, if only they had had the bullets—and the guns that the Nationalists had turned on their own countrymen. . . .'

The guerillas were caught between two fires. If they retreated further south, they would inevitably fall into the hands of the Central Government troops—and they had evidence enough of what that would mean for them. If they turned about and retraced their steps northwards, the Japs awaited them.

'We feel we are caught in a trap—a devil's trap,' wrote Giovanni. 'There is an awful sense of bitterness about the camp. Every man feels that he has fought in vain and that he has none but enemies in the world. Yet there is none who would think of surrender to either opponent. These men are true soldiers devoted to their cause, which they see as the liberty of China and her people. With their bare hands, I think, they would, if called upon, make battle against the combined forces of Japan and the Kuomintang. . . .'

It was a bewildered and fatigued army to which Giovanni belonged; but it was part of a big organization— the Communists of China—and now, at their blackest hour, that body was to give them fresh life and hope. This is how Giovanni recorded the event:

'After nearly a week of despair and indecision, a remarkable thing happened today. An aeroplane was seen to land not far off, and naturally it was assumed to be either Japanese or Nationalist, for we have none. A detachment went out to investigate. They returned with two men who came not as prisoners but on the friendliest of terms with the guerillas. The visitors were taken straight to Tsin, with whom they remained for an hour or more. Then Butts, I, and several Chinese officers were summoned. Tsin stood up and addressed us. He told us that we had

o   209

had orders from G.H.Q., and we all came to attention as he read from the scroll he held in his hand. He said: "This is from Chinese Communist Central Headquarters. So it is headed. The order runs 'Proceed with all speed south and west in the direction of Yenan. Avoid all actions as far as possible with Nationalist forces'. That is all. We march tonight."

'I did not understand it. Nor did the others. And when the news was passed round, there was a sigh of relief. The rise in spirits was unmistakable. It was not that the men knew what the order meant any more than we did. What cheered them was the sudden knowledge that they were not forgotten. . . .'

Chapter Nineteen

THE END OF THE MARCH

I solated with the remnants of the Communist guerillas in remote north-eastern China, Giovanni could have little idea of the significant events that were taking place far to the south—events that, in the final issue, were to bring an entirely new complexion to the Chinese political scene. The message from headquarters ordering a retreat towards Yenan was to him, as to his comrades, a puzzling, even inexplicable, one, but it had to be obeyed. In fact, it was the first news they had of that great event in Chinese Communist history known as the Long March.

In southern and eastern China, the Central Government forces, employing all their vast superiority, had fought a progressively more successful campaign against the Communists, whom they detested with as much—some people said more—ardour as they kept for the Japanese. Step by step they had pressed the Communists back south of the Yangtze. In the towns Communism had been driven underground, but it still more than held its strength in the agricultural area—which meant the greater and more important part of China, which is founded on its peasants. The peasants had gained little from the Nationalist Government and that phase of the Revolution which it represented beyond words and promises for which they could see little evidence of fulfilment. They still squirmed under the extortions of the local war lords and landlords, who had now become the agents for the new authority. The Communists promised the peasants the land for themselves, and wherever their writ ran they did a good deal to implement their intentions. For a government such as Chiang Kai-shek's, determined to have its own way throughout the entire country, this was intolerable. United China meant for the Kuomintang a China completely directed by itself. Opposition could not be tolerated. And every effort was directed towards suppressing the Communists by force.

No doubt this was an over-simplified picture of the state of affairs but it gives the essential background against which the subsequent passages from Giovanni's diaries must be seen; and it provides the departure point for the historical event of the Long March.

In 1934–5, the Nationalists had been so successful that they had virtually penned in the Communists to a comparatively small area south of the Yangtze. It was a tight blockade which, even though practically every part of China can be self-supporting, must inevitably bring them total victory in the long run. Guerilla warfare, which the Communists had brought to a fine art, had continued, but its effectiveness grew less and less as the Nationalists settled down to a policy of waiting in established positions. It was in these circumstances that the Communist High Command made the decision to disengage. With a combination of brilliant tactical planning and untold heroism on the part of those concerned—one cannot say their armies, for civilians as well took part—the Communists broke through the Nationalist cordon and struck west. Thirty thousand people—men, women, and children, with all their impedimenta—were engaged; and they marched. They marched ceaselessly, striking first west and then north, until by the end of 1935, they had established themselves with Yenan in Shensi as their chief centre. This is undoubtedly one of the epic marches of history, long to be remembered in the annals of man's endurance. It covered, under appalling conditions, no less than six thousand miles, and was accomplished by a force deficient in practically every modern means of transport. The Nationalists did all they could to arrest it, but their success in this aim was limited. The Long March went on. Yet curiously, as time was to show, it marked not only the peak of Communist achievement but also a decline of Communist popularity in the countryside. It brought with it savage war and immense hardship for the peaceful peasants through whose land Red and Nationalist troops fought mercilessly. For this, bitter, hostile feelings were aroused.

But it is time to turn from these few words of background explanation to the diaries of Giovanni Campo—those diaries so oddly composed which reached me, Heaven knows how, in all manner of packets, sometimes so slim as to be little more than letters, at others considerable parcels. He records that the early phases of the march towards Yenan were uneventful. As they moved away from their recent scene of operations, the country grew quiet again, with no evidence of the bitter wars that were ravaging China, in the north with the Japs, in the south with their own countrymen.

'Marching along in peace these last few days,' he wrote, 'I am looking at a new China, a China I have never seen before. When I worked with the missions, I was nearer the coast and the hand of Westernization had already changed the way of life. In the north-east it had been war and death and suffering. Here I imagine I am looking at China as it has always been, a land of peasants, a land in which almost the only power available is human muscle, a land living as it has lived for centuries. . . .'

He is stirred by the conditions he finds:

'A journey like this is sufficient to kill stone dead any lingering ideas one may have of the "romance of China". The beautiful things one sees in the museums and art galleries are not Chinese but the products of a small ruling clique that was almost entirely alien to the people. Here one finds only filth, ignorance, and suffering. Perhaps there are ten or twelve huts in the village—though huts is almost too dignified a name to give them with their crude walls of adobe, which, except in the most prosperous places—and there are few prosperous places today in China—are crumbling away and brown with dirt and age. These ten hovels are built together as closely as possible, so that sometimes the rafters of their roofs practically touch each other. Within is a floor of beaten earth. I have read all about this. I have seen it before, but never till now as an established, enduring, integral part of the scene. It is profoundly shocking and saddening that human beings must live like this.

'Yet they live. They break every law of hygiene, but still they live and breed. They breed profusely despite the poor yield that their everlasting labour throughout every minute of every daylight hour brings them from their land. Plague, cholera, floods, and famine—not mere shortages but stark famine—are the natural agencies that keep this fertility within bounds. Infantile mortality is, I imagine, the highest in the world. There is stench everywhere, for the huts are shared with such beasts as the peasant possesses and serve also as granaries. Every scrap of faeces, whether of man or beast, is preserved in pits. This is the one source of essential nitrogen for the soil. The land demands it, and to the Chinese peasant the needs of the land override all else. And these pits, foul beyond description, the happy breeding ground of every kind of micro-organism, are at once the source of life and death for the Chinese. Without their nauseous contents, there would be no crops. And, by the same token, without them there would be less cholera, fewer epidemics.

'Butts, like all young Communists from the West, is full of statistics and plans and fired by visions of the beautiful pictures he has seen of the Soviet collective farms. He looks on all this and grows angry, talking of tractors and scientific farming and co-operative marketing. But I wonder if that is the only solution, whether all that modern civilization has to offer is substitution of slavery to the machine for slavery to the land. . . .'

During this period of comparative calm and inactivity, the diaries become less regular and the few entries are

tinged with rather pessimistic introspection. He talks of
his helplessness:

'Day after day, I become increasingly conscious of my
failure and my impotence. The squalor goes on wherever
we find ourselves. Some of the bigger villages are not at all
unattractive when seen from a distance. The group of
huts is surrounded by a wall. The huts themselves gleam
whitely in the sun. But when one draws near one finds it
only a façade. There are the same stenches, the same
cesspits. . . .

'I came here hoping to do something for these people,
but it is not one man's job, nor could a thousand do it.
What is needed is a new way of life. Before the doctor can
begin to do his work, ignorance and superstition must die.
There must be organization. A medical mission, a million
medical missions can do nothing against the malnutrition
that almost every peasant reveals. They cannot even
fight the rampant diseases without adequate supplies,
which cannot be brought to them unless roads, and rail-
ways, and aerodromes, are built. These are the tasks of
government—and in the face of that need the Chinese
fight amongst themselves while the Japs threaten to take
away, for their own uses, even the little that these pathetic
peasants have. For myself I would not care what government reigned so long as it did those things which would
begin to create a real new China in which men and women
would be free to live as human beings. It could be Communist or Kuomintang or anything else. I would even
support the Japs if I believed that they would do what
is necessary. . . .'

This intermission did not last long. As the column fell
back south and west, it advanced more and more warily.
This was country in which Nationalist troops might be
expected, and while the latter were likely to withdraw at
the sight of Japanese, they would not hesitate to throw
their full weight against any Communist detachment. The
entries become punctuated with descriptions of minor
skirmishes of no particular note—skirmishes marked by

the ruthless savagery to which Giovanni had grown accustomed if not inured. There is a growing hint of weariness and disillusion, and Lydia was worrying him.

'It is difficult to recognize Lydia these days,' he observes. 'Up there, when danger was about us, she was almost gay. Her brightness and resolution were a source of never-ending joy and inspiration to me—and I think, also to Butts and even the Chinese themselves, once they had grown used to the idea of a woman working among them as a man. But now she is morose and taciturn. She spends hours by herself in silence as though she is trying to resolve some weighty problem, and she will not take me into her confidence, which is perhaps the greatest worry of all. I suppose this is what I ought to have expected. This march goes on endlessly. We have been months on the road now, and everywhere spirits are sagging. For Lydia it must be a deeper hell than for any of us—she who is so full of vitality and ambition. Yet she never complains. However she may have seemed to have changed in other things, her courage, as always, is unfailing. . . .'

And a little later:

'The monotony of the march was broken today by a personal incident which is giving me much food for thought, and I am even inclined to panic because I can find no explanation for it. Lydia and I were trudging along side by side, and the road, if one can call it that, seemed to stretch on before us into infinity, with no sign of habitation or vegetation—a fact that enabled us to relax precautions a little for there was no chance of an ambush. Suddenly, after a long silence, she began to speak to me in a low voice that was nearly a whisper. "I'm sorry, Giovanni," she said. I asked her what for, and it took her quite a little while to reply, but at last she told me she was sorry for having brought me into all this, that we ought to have gone to the south and seen what we could do there. I tried to put her doubts at rest, saying that if apologies were needed they were from me to her, for it was I who had permitted her to endure it all. She insisted

216

that it was her fault. There were tears in her eyes, too, and it is unusual nowadays for Lydia to weep. She has become hard, strong, self-controlled to an extent she never was before. When I tried to comfort her she would have none of it. "I have ruined you," she said; and then after a pause she added: "Then I must try to put things right." She would say no more, but this evening she has been very tender to me in a wistful sort of way, almost as though we were going to part, and the very thought of that fills me with dismay. There is one thing I know more clearly now than ever before: I could not live without Lydia. The only parting there can be between us is death. . . .'

Occasional skirmishes with small bands of Nationalist troops occurred and there was trouble with forces belonging to war lords, who had made common cause with the Nationalists in their opposition to the Communists. Casualties on these occasions were slight, for the fighting does not appear to have been serious. More crippling were the deaths caused by the conditions of the march:

'Our state grows worse every day. The best news is that Tsin tells me we may end our journey a little north-east of Yenan at a Communist base in about a fortnight's time. After all these months, a fortnight seems like tomorrow. But I wonder how many of us can survive even fourteen more days of this hell. Our food supplies are barely enough to keep us alive, let alone provide us with sufficient energy for this gruelling march. Men fall out of the column every few minutes. It is a curious sight which horrified me at first but now, such is the callousness of human nature, I take for granted. They stumble, roll out of the way, and almost before I can reach them—it is difficult to hurry—they are dead. There is no suffering. The human system just stops abruptly like an electric lamp which has been suddenly deprived of current.

'Most of the men are now marching in their bare feet. A little while ago Lydia and Butts and I reviewed our footwear and we are rather proud of the results. By pooling the wrecks of our boots, we managed to make up quite a reasonable pair of shoes for Lydia, which have stood up to the strain well, though it will be a miracle if they endure another fortnight. Butts and I have done some intricate cobbling with cardboard, bark, and grass, to provide our feet with something to walk on.

'We have little drinking water now. This area is going through one of its periodic droughts. We have not washed for so long that I cannot remember the last occasion—and the innumerable parasites of China do not need the encouragement of a dirty body to make themselves busy. Men are falling ill with strange conditions that I cannot diagnose, and even if I could, that would not help, for apart from a few bandages, a little iodine, a carefully treasured phial of morphine, and one or two odds and ends, my medical chest is empty. . . .'

Yet despite everything the column marched on—and it won through. There is no paean of joy in Giovanni's record of the arrival at the Yenan base:

'We are here at last. I imagined the arrival would fill us with exultation, but we feel nothing but weariness. As yet I myself have had not even a reaction of relief, and that applies also, I believe, to Lydia and Butts. There is to be an official welcome and celebration tomorrow with banners and Heaven knows what, but I doubt if I shall be there. We shall sleep. That is the best thanksgiving of all. And what, indeed, is there to celebrate? We began the march with just over three thousand men. Six hundred and fifty-two walking skeletons stumbled into the camp today, all of them without boots, the majority of them practically without clothes. The only things they had clung to throughout nine long months of hell were their rifles and their ammunition pouches. That is the Chinese guerilla. The bones of the rest are marking our trail across China. From the south other columns, originally many times the strength of ours, are approaching. God alone knows, in His Wisdom, what condition they will be in. We have been greeted as heroes, but we are really the vanquished. Over the provinces where we fought and suffered, Japanese rule holds sway. Perhaps one day their flag will flutter over all China. Yet when I think of what these men have done, what they have endured, and how they have fought, I do not think so. Governments may submit, treaties may be written, but the people of China will never renounce their own. The Japs have done something which no revolution, no political propaganda, could have done. They have roused the ordinary Chinese peasant and soldier, the man who *is* China, to a sense of heritage and an urge to betterment. That will probably remain for ever as the greatest achievement of the Japanese; the memory of it and its results will far outlast the tale of their victories in the field, their conquests, and even their atrocities. . . .'

Chapter Twenty

WAR

'Even a doctor has to admit,' wrote Giovanni a little later, 'that rest is the best medicine of all. Though it is only a fortnight since I have been at the base, I already feel a new man and am almost ready for anything, though I still have moments of intense weariness, and I know that it will be a long time before any of us Europeans recover completely from the effects of those months of rice, rice, rice. Not that the food here is wonderful. There is still too much rice, but some variety is possible.

'Remarkable as my recovery has been, it is by no means as complete or as rapid as Lydia's. Within a week she seemed to have shaken off all the effects of her fatigue and she became more her normal brisk and cheerful self. She has been busy, too. I was still lolling about my hut when she was calling on General Mao-Hung, the commander here, to present our compliments, and since then she has been with him almost daily. She tells me not to worry as she thinks he will offer me a good position in the Chinese Red Army. . . .'

Lydia was apparently hard at work on her schemes to get herself into the inner councils of the leaders and assure for Giovanni and herself distinguished rank. She did not fail in her efforts, for Giovanni continues:

'I have seen Hung myself now and find him an admirable man. He has a forthrightness about him which is unusual in a Chinese. My first call was entirely formal. Yesterday he sent for me again. Once more he thanked me for what I had done with the guerillas—though he had been fulsome enough about that on the previous occasion —and now he asked me if I wished to continue in the service of the Communist Army. I had already talked this point over with Lydia and she had been insistent that, for the time being at any rate, it was the best thing to do; not only that, it was, as I myself pointed out, the only course open to me. So I answered him in the affirmative, and he seemed very pleased.

'He told me that the guerilla forces were now absorbed into the main Chinese Red Army, which, when its full withdrawal from the south was completed, would establish its headquarters at Yenan. One of its first tasks would be to set up a proper medical service for the whole Army, and the prospects were bright, for the main force included a large number of students from the Chinese universities, as well as a considerable number of volunteer foreign workers, some of them qualified. He suggested I might like to take part in the training and organization.

' "You are a man of action, I know," he said, "but it would be waste of your talents to send you out again as a field surgeon. Red China is not so rich in doctors that she can attach men of high qualifications like yourself to actual front-line units. Besides you have gained unique experience as a guerilla surgeon, and we need your knowledge to pass on to the others. We need to move swiftly, too. There is likely to be fighting before very long."

'This led him on to give me a brief outline of events as he saw them. The Nationalist Government had taken fright when the Red Army had broken out and begun its withdrawal towards Yenan, from which point the Communists would control, if they established themselves there, some of the richest resources in China. In command of that area, the Reds could no longer be regarded as rebels but as a very serious threat to the Nationalists. For this reason, armies were being moved into the plain of Sian, the strategic key to the whole district, and then the policy of blockade and containment would be resumed. These troops, the general pointed out, were not strictly

first impressions, both personal and professional—he is a
graduate of Yale and Columbia—I told Lydia all that had
happened. To my surprise she began to warn me. She told
me I must not get too entangled in Communist politics,
for that would be fatal, and that I was beginning to accept
their view of things as the whole truth, which she did not
think it was. "No one has all the virtues," she pointed out.
I must retain my independence of mind. I had not realized,
till she spoke, how much I had fallen under the persuasive
spell of these men, but, on reflecting upon it, I find that
Lydia's caution was none too soon. As always she is level-
headed and perfectly right. . . .'

He was very soon to have striking evidence of the truth
of Lydia's statement that 'no one had all the virtues'.
With the guerillas he had seen what the Nationalist troops
did when they came across a village sympathetic to the
Reds. Now he was to find that Communist ideology did
little to change Chinese methods. There was an action with
Nationalist troops a comparatively short distance away,
and one of the newly formed medical units was dispatched
at once to the theatre of operations. Giovanni went with it
to see how his training and advice stood up to actual practical test. Until this action he seems to have held the view,
as numerous hints in the pages of the diary show, that the
Reds fought their fellow Chinese only with the greatest
reluctance and inflicted no more damage than was called
for in the interests of their own safety. After all, as he
himself put it, they stood for the Chinese people. On his
return, he made the following entry:

'It has been a shattering experience during which I have
lost many illusions that I had unconsciously built up
during my long association with the Communists. There is
no difference between their methods and the Nationalists',
except that their ruthlessness is vented on a different
object. The Nationalists massacre the peasants whom they
believe to be on the side of the Communists. The Reds, on
the other hand, spare the peasants, to gain their favour,
and massacre all those associated with the landholding and

official classes, merchants and so on, without even the formality of inquiring about their political sympathies. If he is not obviously a peasant or a worker, he is automatically an enemy for whom swift death is insufficient punishment. We took no prisoners.

'On the way back one of the young Chinese doctors related with great satisfaction how he had abandoned an emergency operation half way through on being informed that there had been a mistake and that the patient was a Nationalist officer. This made me feel physically sick, but I have learnt too much of the Chinese mentality even to try to protest. One thing I have yet to discover is whether the Chinese are capable of love. I know only too well how they can hate. . . .'

Perhaps it was a salutary lesson, a brutal means of enabling him to regain his equilibrium of judgment. The tales of the Long March which he heard no longer impressed him as epics of heroism; he saw them now as records of ferocious savagery. Rumours that he previously discredited to the effect that the peasants were beginning to hate Communist troops no less than Nationalists as bloody-clawed tigers now gained a greater likelihood in his sight. But the Communists still strove to show the world in general and the people of China in particular that they stood for the higher unity of the country, and that it was the unyielding attitude of the Kuomintang that stood in the way of consolidation. Manifestos calling upon the Nationalists to call off the civil war and ally themselves to the Communists to fight Japan were poured out unceasingly—and they were not without effect. Giovanni began to see this for himself. He wrote:

'There is a subtle change coming over the whole situation. Much of the sting is going out of the war up here, and Nationalists and Communists seem to be drawing slowly together. I went down to some of our outposts during the past few days, places where our men stand almost face to face with troops under Hsueh-Liang. I found sentry points unmanned and a general atmosphere of relaxation. The officers took no notice of this slackness, a point I could not understand at first. Then a curious thing happened. A party of Nationalist soldiers came towards our positions—so bad a look-out was being kept that I think I was the first to draw attention to them— and of course I expected a general stand-to to action stations. Instead, our men waved to the others. The Nationalists brought several bundles with them, which turned out to contain various kinds of clothing of American manufacture which they proceeded to trade for grain, which is more easily to be had on this side of the front than the other. I am told that this sort of fraternization is increasing, and is winked at by both commands—even encouraged. Both sides are convinced that it is better to save their bullets for the Japanese rather than waste them on each other. A sound and rational view, which ought to spread to higher circles. . . .'

Eventually it did spread and in a dramatic way, but not before Giovanni was to have another glimpse of the curious involutions of Chinese politics. He had been to a conference with Hung on the subject of medical supplies, which were unsatisfactory both in quantity and quality.

'I knew Hung had been to Russia and studied Soviet methods; he had often told me about them,' Giovanni wrote, 'and in my innocence I had assumed that the Communist forces in China naturally drew support and inspiration from Moscow. Thinking on these lines, I raised the question of getting supplies from Russia. Hung looked at me in a most disparaging way. He pointed out that Chiang Kai-shek had healed his breach with Moscow and friendly relations had been re-established between the Russians and the Nationalist Government. The Chinese Communists were entirely independent and could expect no aid from Russia. I must confess that this drove me into an astounded silence. Truly, politics are quite beyond me. . . .'

Day by day the fraternization of the North-western Nationalist Armies and the Reds increased. Officers of the former visited Yenan and were entertained by Communist leaders. There were unofficial discussions of plans to proceed against the Japs, who were ruining northern China by 'peaceful' methods. Smuggling of all kinds, including opium was fostered by the Japs as well as other illegal practices, with the result that money was becoming valueless and crime of all kinds was sweeping aside all authority. No doubt when conditions were sufficiently bad 'Manchukuo' would move to re-establish order on her borders, and so Japanese control would shift a little further south for the process to be repeated.

'The place is alive with rumours,' records Giovanni at this time. 'Everyone says that Chiang Kai-shek is himself flying to Sian to investigate a position that Nanking does not like at all. Hsueh-Liang is going to meet him, the rumour-mongers say, and they are so insistent and in general agreement, except on details, that there is probably some truth in it. . . .'

There was indeed truth in it, for the talk presaged one of the most fantastic episodes in the ever-fantastic history of modern China. Chiang arrived in Sian, presumably to reprimand Hsueh-Liang and his fraternizing troops—and he was promptly put under arrest by the war-lords who had, up till then, supported him. Precisely what happened no one knows for sure, and probably never will, for secrecy is the only consistent thing in Chinese politics. But in the end there was a remarkable volte-face. Though the Reds had taken no ostensible part in these strange affairs, Chiang Kai-shek agreed to call off the Civil War, to meet the Communist leaders for the first time in a decade, and give official recognition to Communist control of the north-west under nominal suzerainty of Nanking. Almost overnight the breach was healed and the stage set for a united drive against Japan.

The news spread like wildfire in Yenan, where it was received with rejoicing.

'Everywhere,' records Giovanni, 'the sensational news is being hailed as a great Communist victory. The Reds claim that it is they who have united China to fight the common menace, and there is certainly a great deal of superficial truth in their claim. They point out that what forced the issue was not the Red strength but the rebellion of the National Northwestern armies against Chiang's policy. I can scarcely believe it, nor can I see where it will lead. . . .'

He could not see that amazing development which, typically Chinese, led Hsueh-Liang, who had gained his point, to allow himself to be arrested and taken back to Nanking for trial for mutiny. But he does set down what the change meant to his own personal standing. A short while afterwards, this entry occurs:

'Only a little while ago, I held a somewhat dubious position as an adviser on medical-service matters to a rebel army, and no doubt if I had been caught by the Nationalists I should have been severely dealt with in my dual role of revolutionary and foreigner. Now all that is changed. Respectability has fallen on me in the twinkle of an eyelid. The rebel Red Army has become the Chinese Eighth Route Army, charged with the responsibility for guerilla warfare against the Japanese. I myself am appointed Medical Adviser in Chief to Headquarters, Eighth Route Army, and already I have had conferences with medical officers of high rank from the Nationalist Northwest Armies. . . .'

The Eighth Route Army went into action almost at once. Japan, taking fright at this sudden coalition of all the available forces in China, including the Communist guerillas which she feared above all for their skill and ferocity, and seeing form before her eyes the long-dreaded bogey of a united China, provoked an incident in Peiping, the ancient Imperial Chinese capital she had occupied some time before. The 'incidents' were over. It was war—a war that was eventually to engulf the whole world.

PART FOUR

Chapter Twenty-one

JOURNEY TO CHUNGKING

This is a history neither of modern China nor of the Chinese war; it is the story of one man whose life was bound up with events in China during one of the most eventful decades of Chinese history—the story as seen largely through his own eyes and recorded in his own diaries. I add my comments only when they seem necessary for clarification or to set the scene—and I make no claim either to absolute accuracy or to deep penetration. As to accuracy, who can know the truth about modern China, a land whose climate encourages the lush growth of intrigue to the virtual exclusion of other and less exotic plants? So I shall pass rapidly over those first few months of China's war. Giovanni reports on events, but mainly at secondhand, and what he writes is of little importance for the development of this narrative. He saw brutalities. He was the witness of stupidities. He had to give his grudging consent to turns of policy with which, in his heart, he disagreed. He held an official position; and in China an office-holder has even less opportunity of expressing his personal opinions and beliefs than elsewhere.

One thing, however, emerges from a mass of diary entries that are otherwise of no particular interest either historically or personally. That is the gradual alteration in Giovanni's outlook and character. I had known him as a man who, once he had formed an opinion—which he did not do lightly—maintained it in the face of all opposition. Above all he was an apostle of intellectual honesty. But now he had come more and more to adopt a policy of what is euphemistically termed 'realism'—though all too often that means little more than trimming one's sails to the prevailing wind. My own prejudice suggests that it was Lydia who was the motive power of this change. If reason and ingrained honesty pointed to one course and Lydia to another, Giovanni would automatically follow the latter. Yet he was not without doubts.

'There are moments when I am profoundly disturbed and unhappy,' he reflects in one entry. 'My position is strong, yet not strong enough for me to contest or even criticize directives from the higher commands. But I have no alternative to agreement. If I wanted to leave I could not, and there would be small enough hope of my getting any sort of worth-while position elsewhere in the world. There was a time when I would have been content with anything so long as I had full opportunities for practising medicine and perhaps doing a little unambitious research on my own into problems in which I am interested. On occasions I still experience that hankering. But conditions are different. There is Lydia to consider, and her happiness and welfare are above all things. I would not sacrifice one iota of them for any amount of purely personal satisfaction for myself. Indeed that contrast or antinomy does not arise. My personal satisfaction and Lydia's happiness are one and the same thing. Purely selfish gratification, whether it be physical or mental, is the lowest depth to which a human being can sink. . . .'

He considers his position in this light:

'I have been thinking again and again anxiously of what the future holds. For the moment I am tied here, where there seems little enough prospect of advancement. Yet I cannot close my eyes to the fact that this alliance between the Nationalists and the Reds is an uneasy combination that might break up as suddenly as it formed. The withdrawal of the Japanese threat or a run of Japanese successes might make all the difference; and whatever happens I cannot see the Communists becoming the rulers of a truly United China. Chiang Kai-shek has the whiphand now. He is the national leader in the campaign against Japan, and it is he who will receive whatever foreign support and supplies that are available, which he can issue to or withhold from the Reds as he thinks fit. He can make them toe the line almost without effort. I feel that my position is held on sufferance. I have been taken over as part of the deal between the two parties and my individual value is small. I suppose I shall have to devise ways and means of making myself *personally* indispensable to whatever group seems most likely to remain in the control of affairs. . . .'

A few years earlier, Giovanni could not have written such a passage; he would have regarded it as beneath contempt. Now he was talking the language of the place-hunter and the careerist. He was not concerned with the efficiency of the service to which he was attached in a high position; he was thinking of the stability and value of that position in itself. Again my bias attributes the change to Lydia, but I may be unfair to some extent. Years in China, a land of favour and intrigue, may not have been without its influence even on Giovanni, whose singleness of purpose I had always admired. And already, in the matter of Communist propaganda, he had revealed himself not altogether proof against the suggestion of environment, and naturally he discussed the matter with Lydia, as he records:

'At last I have had the courage to raise my doubts and anxieties with Lydia. I was not altogether surprised to find that she shared them to the full, nor that she had some excellent suggestions to offer as regards future conduct. She says, very wisely, that it does not do to run ahead too fast; it is fatally easy to jump out of the frying-pan into the fire—and our particular frying-pan is not too uncomfortable at the moment, for we have good quarters and can command almost anything we need, besides enjoying the full confidence of our colleagues in the higher ranks. There is no assurance yet, she pointed out, that the

Kuomintang can fasten themselves on China as the sole authority. Things are not going too well in the Japanese campaign in the east. Everywhere the Chinese are falling back, and their supply position is terrible, though they are showing great resource in removing factories and the like inland out of Japanese reach. The Kuomintang say that their retreats are strategical, that they are delaying and not trying to fight a conclusive action with the Japs. Chiang Kai-shek himself calls it "trading space for time". Perhaps there is something in it, but, as Lydia says, one cannot be at all sure at this stage. And if the Nationalist Armies in the west are crushed that leaves the Communists up here as the sole authority in China. This conversation has lifted a certain amount of weight from my mind. It is always stimulating to have Lydia's informed and balanced views. . . .'

Yes, he had travelled fast and far from his original attitude to life. I wondered how genuine the change was, for over and over again there were hints of regret for the days that had passed, such as this:

'It is one continual fight against everyone else. Supplies of all kinds are short and as soon as a convoy arrives it is each man for himself. Every one of the Medical Directorate has his own pet sector to which he thinks supplies should be sent. As Adviser I have no real authority, but for all that, I do manage sometimes to short-circuit consignments "captured" for some place I know is overstocked and redirect them to where they are really wanted. I can't help wondering whether all this is worth while. I had less worries with the guerillas, and on the whole I think everyone was happier. War is remote from this place. Few think of it as something grim and horrifying which is actually happening. It is just a game, a battle of wits, with recognition and honours and place as the prizes. . . .'

While Giovanni was indulging in this battle of wits and fighting like a dog for his share of the bone, the war was rolling on savagely enough against the Chinese armies.

Whether it was due to superior Japanese strength and strategy or to subtle long-term plans on the part of the Chinese High Command, the fact remained that every bulletin brought news of fresh Chinese reverses. China was turning inwards on herself, away from the false prosperity of the coast and rediscovering her true self in the peasant lands. In due time, the focus of this convergence became Chungking, and when Chiang Kai-shek had established his capital there, Giovanni and Lydia turned their eyes towards it. For with that removal, as all commentators agree, a new spirit came over China. Then it was that this land of intrigue came truly united, if only for a brief space, and Chungking, to all intents and purposes undefended, suffering continuous and barbarous attacks from the air, became a symbol of hope and resistance to all China. Even the Communists in the north-west, the Eighth Route Army, spoke of the wartime capital with respect and accepted its leadership. This was the moment for Giovanni to strike.

'It seems that China is really united at last,' he wrote. 'It is strange to see the Reds accepting orders from Chungking almost without question, as though they come from an inspired temple, but they do so, and it is a sign for the good. I feel that my place is there—and so does Lydia. We are wasting our time here. There is nothing now for me to do. The medical services, such as they are, are running themselves, and I am a mere superfluous hanger-on, for there is nothing else to which I could turn my hand. The question is how I am to get there and what sort of welcome would await me there. Lydia has ideas, and she is going to put them informally to Hung, who is always ready to listen to her. Because of my official standing, he has to be more reserved with me. . . .'

As might have been expected, when Lydia went into action the results were not unsatisfactory:

'Lydia reports good progress with Hung,' says Giovanni of this episode. 'She is tackling him on the question of medical supplies. There are reports of considerable

American consignments reaching the country but we see none of them, and the British, too, are supposed to be helping in this respect. By gentle suggestion, Lydia is putting it to Hung that what he needs is a representative on the spot in Chungking to see that we get our share; she leaves him, for the time being, to make the obvious inference that I am the most suitable person to send, for the simple reason that, as a foreigner, I would not have any particular axe to grind. . . .'

He took this form of intrigue in his stride; it was the only way of achieving anything in China. If Lydia charmed Hung, as she no doubt did, it was quite in order to turn that fact to good account. But that is the rule all the world over. No business man has a bigger asset than a fascinating wife. Of a subsequent committee meeting, Giovanni records:

'For the first time for some weeks Hung himself presided. He said he wanted to raise the question of medical supplies, and it rather amused me, though I did not show it, to hear him putting forward, as his own original thoughts, all the arguments that Lydia has been pressing on him. He went no further than the general outline, but I am in high hopes, in view of his attitude, that he has me in mind. I am tired of kicking my heels here. . . .'

Eventually the scheme succeeded. Hung sent for Giovanni and told him he had been appointed to go to Chungking and take a hand in the scramble for medical supplies. He was to leave at the earliest possible moment, with a suitable escort, and it might be possible to arrange for him to fly part of the way. This decision was arrived at without reference to the committee on medical services —probably Lydia had applied the final pressure—and it created a certain amount of heartburning, as Giovanni dutifully records:

'I was overjoyed when Hung told me I was to go. He made the appointment in his capacity as supreme local commander and so the approval of the committee was not necessary. Nevertheless, some of the Chinese are up in arms about it, and I am very glad indeed that I am to leave at once. This place might become a little unhealthy for me if I remained much longer. The arguments against me are, first that I have and can have no real rank or authority as a foreigner; secondly that it is obviously a job for Chinese who alone can deal satisfactorily with other Chinese, as well as a lot of personal objections and hurt pride. Hung refuses to alter his decision or even reconsider it. He is convinced that he is right, and the more opposition grows, the firmer he will remain. That is his way. He has dismissed the arguments by saying that I shall be better able to deal with the American supply authorities. How that turns out, and even whether I have to deal with them at all, time alone can show. The main point is that we are going to Chungking, the very heart of things, where we can think about the future and get a better idea of how matters are going in China. There is only one snag—whether Chungking will accept me in my assigned role. But that again is not of overwhelming importance, provided I am not turned back before reaching the capital or am refused admission. . . .'

He was lucky in the journey. After a day's march, the escort reached an army aerodrome, where it was learnt that a plane was leaving the next day for the neighbourhood of Chungking. Even the march was not as onerous as it might have been. Giovanni and Lydia were no longer guerillas, equals among equals, claiming no privileges over their fellows.

'We are travelling in style this time,' he wrote of the first stage of the journey. 'Even had we wanted to, we could not have gone on foot, for that would have been to lower ourselves and lose face. So we are being carried in chairs. When I think of the unending miles we marched with the guerillas, I am inclined to smile. Is it that I was a different person then, or has experience taught me that nothing comes to those who hide their lights beneath bushels? . . .'

At least he was conscious of the change in himself, though it is noteworthy that he does not reprobate it. He continued:

'Lydia is already planning our moves in Chungking, though, of course, we know very little about conditions in the place, and how affairs are handled there. But we have discussed our main objectives. I agree with her that it will be best, if possible, to obtain a position directly under the Kuomintang Nationalist Government. They do not like the Communists and the alliance is only a marriage of convenience with the divorce court never far away. As a representative of Yenan I should no doubt have formal acceptance but no more, and if the wind changed I should suffer at once for my Communist associations. Once in the government service itself and all this nightmare of doubt and anxiety is over. . . .'

The final phase of the journey had to be made on foot. It was not a very happy experience.

'All China seems to be trying to force its way into Chungking,' he records. 'The roads are crammed. But we are travelling in real style, an American limousine having been put at our disposal. This is a wonderful experience, which almost suggests we are back in civilization after all these years; and it is giving Lydia a great thrill. I can see the sparkle of delight in her eye.

'All went well till we came to one of the inner guard posts, where all credentials are very thoroughly examined. The officer who dealt with us was far from friendly. He looked at my papers and sneered. "A Communist, eh?" he said aggressively. I hastened to reassure him. I was an Italian doctor; I had no interest in Chinese politics; I was trying to do what I could for a country for which, during my years of service to it, I have conceived a great affection. This silenced him, though he still regarded me suspiciously, and he called in someone of superior rank. This man was all courtesy and smiles, though I felt they were insincere. After Lydia had talked to him for a few minutes in fluent Chinese, his smiles broadened and he agreed to let us go into the centre. He even told us where to report to ensure lodgings, which are very difficult to get. Indeed, the streets themselves are so crammed that movement is barely possible. This affair, however, has emphasized the wisdom of the decisions about service that Lydia and I have made. . . .'

It was a strange and unexpected journey Giovanni was making.

Chapter Twenty-two

A NEW APPOINTMENT

Many people have written about Chungking at the time of the Chinese war—its strange contrasts with every one of the many subdivisions of the Chinese people represented, its filth and squalor, its unbelievable overcrowding, and, above all, its tremendous spirit of patriotism that lasted for so short a time. Giovanni added little to these accounts. It is true he recorded the sights and sounds much as others have described them, speaking of the horror of the air-raids and the confusion in the midst of which government business seemed to go on with an efficiency hitherto unknown in Chinese history. In one brief comment he brings his own particular point of view to the fore:

'There are many things to wonder at in Chungking, not least where so many people manage to put themselves. I am told the original population of this fog-ridden ant-hill —one hardly dare call it a city—was no more than two hundred thousand, while today it is round about a million; and every day more and more people—government officials, merchants, foreign missions, Army officers, and who knows what—pour into it. Yet to my mind the greatest wonder of all is that some violent epidemic has not occurred to wipe out the whole of this squirming mass of people.

'Chungking may well be the unhealthiest place in China; I have seen nothing worse, and I am not inexperienced of China, yet the average health appears to be neither lower nor higher than elsewhere in the large cities. There is everything ready to break loose. Cholera and dysentery haunt the valley; syphilis is worse than I have encountered it apart from the coast towns. Despite the fact that every square metre of floor space must be needed for living and sleeping purposes, one can find opium dens almost without looking for them. The Chinese curse of malnutrition and deficiency diseases rests heavily on the people. Here is a mine of disastrous disease, yet by some humane design of Providence it fails to explode. . . .'

When the air-raids started and continued to mount, he returned briefly to the same theme:

'There must indeed be some special Providence watching over Chungking at this time,' he wrote. 'When the two red lights that indicate imminent air-raid danger fall, everyone bolts for the shelters, taking with them all their possessions. They crowd into caves, both natural and artificial, in the living rock; and there, in darkness or semi-darkness, amid dampness, the stink of crammed human bodies, they wait until the all-clear signal is given, when, for a little while, they can breathe again whatever fresh air Chungking has to supply—and that is not much. In these conditions, they rub shoulders with people carrying, I should imagine, every known infectious disease and perhaps not a few unknown as yet to Western research. Yet they continue to live and even to thrive. The native Chungkingites certainly thrive, for to them every one of the three-quarters of a million strangers among them is someone to be swindled, a bringer of loot which it is their duty to extort. . . .'

The remarkable fact is that medical sidelights are so few and far between. One can imagine the plans for investigation of the conditions Giovanni would have had if he had gone there instead of 'kicking his heels', as he put it, in Yenan. But now he was a man with a purpose —and that purpose was his personal preferment. It difficult to write of him as one seeking the fleshpots, but indeed it was. He and Lydia lost no time in getting to w

A New Appointment

After less than a fortnight in Chungking, he made the following observation:

'My position here is now quite plain to me. All my credentials as a representative of Eighth Route Army are practically valueless beyond conferring on me the right to remain in the capital and the nominal privilege of interviewing the officials I want to see. There is little point in that. My designated task here is to organize medical supplies for the north-western troops, and that involves seeing various people who have those supplies under their control. But to approach them, there is a recognized order of precedence. Everyone, it seems, had priority over a representative of the Communist armies—and I had observed that this does not apply to me alone. A 'Red' passport is barely worth the paper it is written on. Perhaps I take my place in the queue for two days without getting a chance to say a word; when at last I am seen—by a minor official—I am told to set out my representations in writing and they will be considered by the proper department. This is government procedure the world over, I suppose, but it is quite clear that there is something more than red tape across my path. . . .'

He describes further handicaps:

'The right way everywhere to the ear of responsible officials is by way of the back door—to obtain a personal introduction, to take the man out to dinner or give him a drink, and then casually mention what one needs. Such back-door methods are the rule rather than the exception. Chungking is a hot-bed of patronage, with Chiang Kai-shek, the Generalissimo, as the final dispenser of all orders and all favours. Anyone who has access to Chiang's private ear holds a position of almost unlimited power. But my status as a suspected Red prevents my working this line of approach. No one wishes to know me. At formal gatherings, I am all but ignored; only Chinese courtesy, which is the most superficial thing in the world, makes my acknowledgment at all possible. I am faced by a desperate situation. My present status cripples me, both for doing the job I have been sent here to do and finding ways to secure another and more enviable one. . . .'

He made one desperate effort to secure the favourable attention of the Russian representatives, despite what Hung had told him of the relations between Moscow and the Chinese Communists. It was abortive, as he might have expected. Russia was, in 1939, walking a tightrope in both Europe and Asia, and her representatives wished to do nothing that might threaten the delicate equilibrium.

But he had a key in reserve that promised to open all locked doors. That was Lydia, and she tackled the problem with her usual acumen. Any sort of direct approach to the Chinese was impossible, equally any attempt to meet them informally was foreordained to failure. She presented her plans to Giovanni. This is how he writes of them:

'In such matters, Lydia has a far better head than I. Naturally she is more acute, and she has had practical experience of politics. I know she has been thinking a good deal of our position here, which she feels keenly. She is not used to being snubbed in public by Chinese. Her first suggestion is that we discourage all contacts with the various Chinese Communists who are here. Naturally, as fellow sufferers, they tend to hang together, and they have frequently sought my company. I could hardly refuse them. But now she counsels a cautious withdrawal from them, not sufficiently marked at first for them to protest to Communist H.Q. and so threaten the cancellation of my mission, but enough to indicate, both publicly and privately, that we do not regard ourselves as belonging to them. This will strengthen my contention that I have nothing to do with politics, but am, as a doctor and a foreigner, quite disinterested. The difficulty there, of course, is that the Chinese are almost incapable constitutionally of admitting the existence of disinterestedness.

'As a second step, she believes we ought to make use of our foreign status. There are many foreigners in the city, to which, of course, all the diplomatic missions have come, and there are traders and others concerned with supplies—and, I suspect, nosing out how they can make a little more profit out of what they call "this war business in China". She regards the Americans as the most likely. At the same time, she advises that we keep fellow Italians at arm's length. Fascism is not popular with Americans and still less with the British, the French, and the Europeans generally other than the Germans. She is going to think out ways of approach. . . .'

This, as might have been foretold, did not take Lydia long. Four days later, Giovanni remarks with some surprise:

'It is a mystery to me how it is that when Lydia makes up her mind to achieve an end, it seems to succeed by itself. It seems only yesterday that we were discussing making contact with the Americans, but only as a possibility. Now she tells me that she has managed to obtain an introduction to one of the officials of the American mission in the city and he is anxious to meet us for dinner. . . .'

Lydia had made promises to the American. He wanted facts about the Communists in north-west China. At first, Giovanni was a little doubtful of the propriety of his discussing official secrets:

'I confess,' he says in the next entry, 'that I am not too happy about this proposal of Lydia's, but it is so unusual for her to blunder or to make rash promises that I feel I must be mistaken and given to baseless qualms. I pointed out to her that it hardly seemed right I should discuss the affairs of the Eighth Route Army with the representative of a foreign power while I was still an official representative of that army and, moreover, nominally still retained a fairly high rank in its Command. But she told me I was being silly. If the American did not get what he wanted from me, he would get it from someone else, probably a Chinese Communist who was not so troubled about codes of conduct that had no value in the Far East. She was quite brusque about it. . . .'

A New Appointment

Her brusqueness dispelled those qualms of his:

'On thinking it over,' he notes later, 'I think perhaps Lydia is right. I have no idea what sort of information the American wants. There was no evidence that it was either secret or confidential. The strength of the Eighth Route Army was widely known, as were its plans for raising that strength to something like a million men in the shortest possible space of time. It was only a small price I was being asked to pay for a connexion that might well have the most profound influence on our future. I could see, furthermore, that Lydia was growing rather dispirited under the cool treatment she was receiving from the Chinese, and that for her sake I had to do something quickly to break out of the ring that hemmed us in. No price is too big to pay for her happiness and peace of mind, and what I was being asked was trivial when that was borne in mind. . . .'

They dined with the American, whose name turned out to be Wyman R. Garrow. He took them to one of the innumerable restaurants that had sprung up in Chungking to meet the needs of the new population, which had brought with them, from all parts of China and beyond, tastes in food with which the native resources were quite unable to deal. Mr. Garrow, with that perfect sense of hospitality that marks the cultured American, managed to find a restaurant that specialized—oddly enough—in Italian cooking. Giovanni and Lydia were enchanted.

'This was a miracle!' he wrote enthusiastically on the day following the dinner. 'Here were dishes, perfectly prepared, that neither of us had seen since we left Italy. The very winds of the Adriatic seemed to blow through the hot, steaming air of the small, ill-lit room. Yet I should not have been surprised, I suppose. Chungking has become a microcosm not only of all China but also of the whole world. The Americans can get their hamburgers, and the English their rump steaks. So why not Italian dishes, since Italian cooking is the finest in the world? There was no drinkable wine in the cellars, but Garrow had foreseen even that. He had brought with him a bottle of *Lacrima Christi*, which I barely dared to drink fearing that it might be the last time I should taste and smell it.

'As for Lydia, this was a glimpse of a departed paradise for her. Her eyes lit up, and the expression of sternness she developed with the guerillas left her, revealing in all her beauty the girl with whom I had fallen so deeply in love in Florence—and whom I still love, perhaps more deeply. This was the most miraculous event of all. I was seeing the vision that transcends all visions. . . .'

From these lyrical and erotic heights, Giovanni descends to the more mundane immediate purpose of the meeting: the possibility of disclosing information. But the business did not go very far at that first meeting; perhaps the whole atmosphere was too full of nostalgic glamour.

'Garrow did not mention our business till the end of the dinner,' comments Giovanni, 'and then only in a rather indirect way. He said he would like to have a business chat with me and made an appointment for me to call at his offices the next day. I was glad that we did not have to discuss it then and there. This is a step forward of some size', he concludes with relish. 'I do not know how my dealings with Garrow will go, but it will be a slap in the eye for the people who have been cold-shouldering me when they see me going as an invited visitor to the American Military Mission. . . .'

The interview proved satisfactory, as he recorded the next day:

'I have been to see Garrow and find him, in business, no less charming than he is as a host. His tact is superb. He clearly realized that I was in a rather equivocal position as a still accredited representative of the "Reds", as he insisted on calling them, and he asked me no direct questions. Instead, he produced several typewritten sheets and asked me to go through them, making any comments I wished as to their accuracy or lack of it. American intelligence must be very good, for there were details on those sheets of the Eighth Route Army strength, dispositions, and equipment, that I thought could be known only to a few of us in the inner circle, and some, in fact, that were news to me and on which I was unable to comment. I said what I thought was wise and true, and he nodded as he put the sheets away. "Thanks a lot, doctor," he said, American fashion. "You've been a real help."

'I am not a negotiator of diplomatic standards, and I was in some difficulty in knowing how to approach my side of the implicit bargain—that if I helped him, he would help me. Once again his fine sensibility came to the rescue. After chatting a little on China generally, he led up to the subject of life in Chungking (which he hated with an intense American hate) and then added, with a significant change of tone, that he understood from my wife—whom he described as a very charming woman, exceptional in both brains and beauty—that I was finding life as a Red representative in Chungking rather irksome.

'This, as I think it was intended to do, gave me my opportunity to unfold my sorrows to him. He listened attentively. When I had finished, he said he quite understood that it must be a terrible thing for me to be mixed up with the Communists and he could well imagine that my greatest ambition would be to get rid of my embarrassing connexions. He hinted that his mission had considerable influence in high Kuomintang circles and perhaps an opportunity would occur for him to help me out of my invidious position. He suggested that we should meet again in his office the day after tomorrow. I am hopeful of the outcome, and so is Lydia, to whom, of course, I made a full report of what happened. . . .'

Giovanni, the incorruptible, as I had always imagined him, was now thoroughly enmeshed in the web of intrigue which, passing for diplomacy in China among all nations, ranges from subtle bribery to plain, unadorned spying and corruption. Though he did not record the actual conversation, Lydia obviously urged him on, as this entry suggests:

A New Appointment

'I set out for my second meeting with Garrow well charged with advice from Lydia, who told me that Americans liked plain speaking once friendly relations had been established and thought very little of men who beat about the bush. I did not think I should have to do any hard bargaining, as it is called, with Garrow, who had shown he had a keen appreciation of the position. I dreaded the possibility of my having to engage in any huckstering. There was no need for these latter fears. He set them at rest almost at once, after the usual polite exchanges, by repeating the very thought that Lydia had given me.

' "Listen, doctor," he said, "I'm an American and I like plain honest man-to-man speaking. You've helped me a lot already, and I think you can help me some more. Let's get this quite clear. If you're ready to tell me all you know, without reservations, I guarantee to get you out of your present jam with a good job in the Government. O.K.?"

'I liked him for that—so very different from the tortuous methods of the Chinese. I hesitated for just a moment, and then said that I would take his word and was ready to strike the bargain. He held out his hand and I grasped it. I felt he could be completely trusted.

'This time he asked me the most searching questions direct. He told me his Government was interested in everything that was happening in China, and that sooner or later affairs between the U.S.A. and Japan would "blow up", as he put it, and then his country and China would be allies, so every scrap of information I could give now would be an eventual help to China. He wanted to know particularly what happened to the stores America was sending. They were supposed to go to all armies fighting the Japs. How much did the Eighth Route Army get?

'I told him what I knew. I could be quite positive about the medical stores. None had ever reached the Eighth Route Army. As for ammunition, which also had been coming through, though not so openly, I could not speak with absolute certainty, but so far as my knowledge went there had never been any American rifles or ammunition with the men, apart from those which had been captured during the period of the Civil War.

'This did not surprise him. He said it agreed with what he thought. He added they would have to find out exactly where the supplies did go. They were certainly being sent out from the ports, and by no means all of them reached the Nationalist armies proper, so far as he could trace. There was a leakage, but where and to whom? Those were, of course, questions I could not answer. When I had told him everything I knew, he again shook my hand, telling me I had done my part of the work and now he was going to do his. He said he would not appear in the matter any more, but I should have a letter about it in a day or two. He did not say from whom the letter would come or what he had in mind. There I had to leave the matter, but I had complete faith that he would redeem his promises to me. . . .'

A more worldly-wise man might have considered Giovanni's faith rather touching and naïve. He would have pointed out that Giovanni had sold all his goods on no security at all and had received in return not even a cheque which might not be honoured. But as it turned out, Giovanni was right, and the worldly-wise would have been wrong. Sometimes simple faith serves better than sophistication. Three days afterwards, the diary contains this item:

'Today the expected letter arrived. Though Garrow is not mentioned in it, I am sure it is the result of his work. It comes from the Secretariat of the Supreme National Defence Council and bids me attend tomorrow for an interview on "an important matter". I am filled with expectations not unmixed with fears. Lydia does not share the latter, but is quite certain that all will be well.'

Lydia, as usual, was right, if by 'well' she meant that the much sought-after Government position would be Giovanni's. But if 'well' could be taken to mean Giovanni's increase of stature as a human being, then his own fears were more justifiable. But these were the facts as set out in the diary:

'I went to the offices of the S.N.D.C. as desired. I have been there before in my status as a humble petitioner for the Eighth Route Army, and I passed into the familiar lobby not without a little sinking of the heart. But this time there was no need to worry. I showed the letter of appointment to the reception clerk, noting out of the corner of my eye several of my former Communist colleagues waiting gloomily on the benches provided for them, and he checked it against a list he had on his desk. Instantly he dispatched a messenger, and a few minutes later I was shown into a small inner office, where there was a small, dark Chinese in conventional Western morning dress. Never before had I experienced such expedition in my dealings with Chinese.

'He addressed me in English, saying he understood I spoke that language and he preferred to use it for business purposes as it was more direct than Chinese, which, however, he said he was aware I spoke perfectly. I bowed at the compliment. Chinese may speak English, but they still regard formality as vital. Then he began talking business. He said that since I had come to Chungking the Council had, as a matter of course, examined my record and been much impressed by it. He reminded me that all Chinese military operations were now under the direction of the Council, which was trying to make the fullest use of the personnel at its disposal, particularly of men of outstanding abilities. Medical personnel were especially valuable, and the Council considered my experience and qualifications were being insufficiently utilized in my present position, which was mainly administrative, etc. etc. So he kept on, making it appear that I had forced myself upon their attention by a blazing brilliance such as would have secured for me the Nobel Prize five years in succession.

'In the end, he made me an offer. The Council would be honoured—so he put it, but this, after all, is China—if I would agree to being attached to the Medical Section of the

Council as an adviser on general medical matters as they affected guerilla warfare, in which I was expert, while also I should be expected to place my medical talents at the disposal of the members of the Government and the Kuomintang. The salary would be sufficient to maintain the state this position demanded and would be worked out by the financial section, and I should be provided with accommodation for myself and my wife—whom he said he was hoping to meet as soon as possible—a car, and other "amenities".

'I thanked him, not effusively, for that would have been bad manners, but with becoming humility and recognition of my unworthiness, and left, feeling a little dazed at my good fortune. Everything had turned out in the best possible manner. I was a subordinate member of the S.N.D.C., the ruling body of China, and honorary physician to the men who governed China. I could still not believe my good fortune. When I told Lydia I was almost incoherent with excitement, while she danced for joy. Once more, as throughout my life in recent years, I owe all to her, who has by her love for me shown me the path to the top. . . .'

But if he plunged deep into troubled seas, Giovanni was still a novice in the finer arts of swimming in them, as this excerpt, written a little later, reveals:

'I felt that I must thank Garrow for his magnificent help in bringing my name before the S.N.D.C., and I sent him a short note asking him to dine one evening with Lydia and myself. To my complete surprise I received a very short note from his secretary in reply, saying rather coldly that Mr. Garrow was very heavily engaged for a long time ahead, and could accept no further engagements. I take this as a distinct rebuff, though I cannot understand it. . . .'

Yes, the 'subordinate member of the S.N.D.C.', as he termed himself, had still a very great deal to learn.

Chapter Twenty-three

THE MAN TRANSFORMED

From this point, Giovanni's life became centred on Chungking, and for him, as for all the people in that seething city, the war became somewhat remote and unreal. While the bombings lasted and danger was ever present, Chungking was a centre of activity and effort. For all China it was the symbol of a country that had sunk all its embittered differences and now stood for united, heroic, and unyielding resistance to the Japanese. Chungking had its hour of glory and wrote its name once more in letters of gold in the history of China; and then, the danger from the air over and the war itself settled into stalemate, it became, true to tradition, a place of cynical jobbery, unscrupulous intrigue, and, at times, forthright treachery.

Giovanni's duties were not very onerous. He writes of them quite early in his Chungking career:

'I have been called upon twice to give a second opinion on a case handled by an American doctor attending one of the members of the S.N.D.C. It was a mere formality, and I hardly know why I was called in unless it was to let me see that I had to justify my position as an honorary physician. Each week I attend a meeting of a special sub-committee on army medicine. There is nothing much involved in this, for as a rule the business consists of agreeing with decisions already made higher up in the hierarchy. Let me say that most of these ready-made decisions are sound and do not call for discussion. Daily I go to my office, where I have two secretaries, one French, and one Chinese, but there is not a great deal to do. Now I am asked to comment on a report upon medical work at some sector of the front, now to make some suggestions on organization or reorganization. Sometimes, at the sub-committee, I can recognize some of my suggestions after modification; but as they are never very original ones, but always seem obvious to me, it may be that they come from someone else and my reports are never read. That would be quite in keeping with the methods here. . . .'

It is an indication of how he has changed that he makes no suggestion of his chafing at this inactivity, as he would have done only a little while earlier. He was content now to take things as they came. Luxury, which once had roused his contemptuous ire, was now part of his life. He took every advantage of his privileges and of the curious state of affairs that existed in China. Thus he says:

'Living in Chungking is not exactly like what I imagine living in Paris or Rome or London might be. The conditions of the town itself make that impossible. There are sometimes acute shortages of certain foods, and in spite of American supplies, European foods are often hard to come by. Yet compared with the way in which we existed for so long with the guerillas, it is something more than luxury. Those days seem very far off and unreal now, and I sometimes find it impossible even to imagine that Lydia and I really experienced them. The conditions appear such as no man—and far more, no woman—could have survived for as long as we did. . . .'

Other means existed, before Pearl Harbour and the fusion of the war in the East with the war in the West, for satisfying his new-found love of luxury. Every night, the Chinese National Airways flew a machine to the British settlement at Hong Kong. Many of the Chinese officials made the journey to obtain a respite from the conditions in the capital, especially during the bombing terror. It became a habit with Giovanni and Lydia. He comments:

'In a few hours, one is transported right away from all the horrors of Chungking and steps into an entirely different world, where there are bright lights, good hotels, clean streets, and all the amenities of civilization. One can dine on what one fancies, drink what one will. It is a treat to be a part of European society again, though, of course, it is predominantly British, and I have yet to hear the familiar sound of an Italian voice. It is strange, too, to remember that England is at war and her people suffering from shortages, while out here in Hong Kong, on the fringe of another war, they lack for nothing. The world is indeed a strange place, and nothing is stranger in it than the changes of fortune it brings to people. . . .'

'Bright lights, good hotels'—was that really Giovanni speaking? It was indeed; and these things had come to fascinate him. Even Chungking had its attractions:

' Almost every night, Lydia and I dine out, more often than not with friends, of whom I am glad to say we lately have many. By now we have tried every one of the many restaurants in the city, each with its own local food, so that I think I have tried all manner of Chinese dishes there may be. I like some of them, but I have come to long for good Italian and French cooking after all these years. Chinese dishes, however good and unfamiliar, remind me too much of those days with the guerillas which now I long to forget. Except perhaps at night, when the poor people have retired to bed, because there is no light in their hovels, it is almost impossible to use my car; the roads are too cluttered with pigs, poultry, and other obstacles living and dead, human and non-human, to make progress tolerable except in a rickshaw. But at times, as when attending a reception or a ceremonial dinner in one of the fine suburbs where the higher officials and members of the Government have their homes, it is necessary for prestige to use it. I am hoping soon to get one of these villas. It is expected to fall vacant in a little while, and I have had my name placed first on the list for it. I never realized before quite how much money and position could do in matters of this kind. . . .'

The Man Transformed

That last sentence shows that naïveté still lingered in him.

In reading the diaries of this period, I have the feeling that they were written by a total stranger. In the earlier letters and diaries, I could almost imagine Giovanni standing before me and telling me by word of mouth the affairs about which he wrote. But this is the work of someone I did not know. There are glimpses of the man I remembered, but they are few, and even then they are distorted. Pages and pages of these entries might just as well never have been written. Descriptions *ad nauseam* of official receptions, with lists of the people present, particularly of the eminent to whom he was introduced or with whom he conversed. The volumes in which these records were made were sumptuous—stiff covers and leather spines and corners, but they contain nothing so striking or as exciting as many of those sheets of wrapping paper, dabbed at with a broken pen, which reached me by devious means from the guerilla war of the north-east.

It is in the few medical entries that the change is most clearly and depressingly marked. He has lost most of his interest in his once beloved profession, though he will describe at length how he was called in to attend this or that minister and of the respect with which he was received. The status of the patient mattered more than the conduct of the case. On the other hand, medical affairs that once would have filled him with an urgent desire to act, to work night and day, left him cold, as this:

'The continuous air-raids have, of course, made the city a wreck. The ruins have become tanks for stagnant water in which mosquitoes breed, so it is not surprising that malaria is becoming a major problem. The water supply is almost non-existent, though some arrangements are made for the better-class parts of the town. What there is is bad, and often infested with parasites. Dysentery is an endemic disease, but it is on the increase, as might be expected. The latest threat is bubonic plague. The rats have ample food supplies among the casualties and the ordure that collects in the ruins; I have never seen the loathsome beasts so fat and bold—they will attack sleeping children.

'Reports on the health of the city come to me sometimes, for the municipal authorities are heavily burdened with their protection systems and are overworked. But there is little I can do about it. Chungking is over-populated—grossly over-populated—and abhorrent conditions are making the preservation of health impossible. The only thing I can do is to make a general report of what *might* be done, adding that I realize it is impossible. The only emergency measures that could be applied would be no more use than bringing a garden hose to a blazing cellulose factory. . . .'

The note of callousness in this is profoundly shocking. Giovanni was unmoved; yet that same Giovanni would— and so recently!—have forgotten sleep, food, everything, on the bare hope of bringing relief to but one of those who were suffering. So strong was the call of luxury and so mute the once strong voice of duty that he could even write this at this same period:

'We flew to Hong Kong again today. On the plane was a Chinese official with whom we talked. It appears he has quite extensive property in Hong Kong, including a fine house to which he has evacuated his wife and family. It is to visit these that he makes this trip as often as he can. Yet he never considers settling in Hong Kong— "not", he said, "until the war is over and I retire". It is his duty to China, he says. So after each short visit he goes back to the shambles of Chungking. He has no financial necessity to do so. The Chinese dollars he earns are almost valueless, so far has inflation gone, while here in Hong Kong he has ample money to live in luxury and ease with his wife and family. I wish I had his chances. I would not be in two minds for a single moment. . . .'

Even the savagery of the Japanese and his hatred of

all they did seems to have been forgotten, and he begins to regard the whole war as a 'sham':

'It is difficult,' he writes, 'to believe that this is a real war. Too many strange things go on. The posts go regularly to places beyond the Japanese lines. American supplies which reach China earmarked for the armies find their way to the Japs, and equally certain Chinese import goods on a profitable basis from Japan. Surely the time has come for all this sham to cease and for those concerned to talk their way to a solution of unreal problems round a conference table. . . .'

In one thing alone had Giovanni remained constant: his utter devotion and admiration for Lydia. He spoke of her still in words of rapture such as a young lover might use in the first realization of his passion. She had enslaved him completely, and the chains she had laid upon him were of unbreakable metal. If they were dragging him down, he did not care. In one self-revealing passage, he says:

'Once I thought I had remained in China because I had developed a deep affection for her people and their ways, and I thought that my destiny lay in helping them to the utmost of my powers. How vainglorious and dramatic are the self-delusions of youth! For now I know the truth, and it is something far greater than any dream of self-sacrificing service and mock heroism in the face of non-existent dangers. I learnt that truth in the stern country of the guerilla war, in the bases of the Eighth Route Army, but most of all here in Chungking, with its smells, its filth, its iniquity, and its tawdry grandeur. That truth is simply that I am in China because Lydia is here. She, with that sagacity and foresight of hers, wished to stay, though the price of remaining seemed heavy. Yet where she was, there must I be. If the hardships of Jehol and Chahar now seem to me unendurable, I know also that I was given the strength to survive them because of my love for Lydia. If I have risen from an obscure medical missionary to one who moves in the highest

circles of the Chinese capital, it is because from Lydia's
love has sprung a strength and an ambition which otherwise I could never have realized. My life is intertwined
with hers, and hers with mine, and if the one shall fail
then will the other falter and die. Lydia has been my eyes
and my ears, my star, and my destiny. Years ago in
Italy, there were some who thought she had deserted
and denied me, and that I must try to forget her. Can a
man forget his own soul? I knew that one day she would
return to me, that in the fullness of time she and I would
make through life our appointed journey together.

'Where the future lies, I do not know. There is war in
China. There is war in Europe. Soon, so those who know
tell me, the two wars will become one, and the whole
world will be ablaze with strife. Yet through it all, Lydia
and I will remain together, and nothing shall part us.
Each night when I pray to God for Lydia's safety, for
Lydia's happiness, I know also that in so doing I pray for
my own; for the two are one. The world is all one to me
so long as Lydia is there. I can think of death—her death
and my death—without a qualm for I know that in death
as in life we shall be together; but I cannot think of
parting, for there can be no parting. Love drives. Love
binds. But never does love—the love such as I bear
Lydia—divide.'

In such phrases, which occur, it is true, only rarely, it is
as though he is pouring out his very soul, like a nightingale
in the pines. The love in him is so vast and swelling that
he can no longer contain it within himself. And curiously,
though all this was part of the Giovanni I had known, it
was the part that had been a stranger to me. I had never
been able to understand this love of his which had made
him step right out of his normal character. It was that
same strange drive which had forced him into his present
unexpected paths. Giovanni the lotos-eater, the place-
seeker, the basker in reflected glory, the sycophant—the
name and the epithets were incompatible. I felt that at
some time the essential Giovanni must emerge from

the burden of accretion which had gathered round him and weighed him down; and when that happened, the unpredictable must occur again. Dimly I began to perceive that already in Giovanni the seeds of tragedy were beginning to germinate. But their time for fruition was not yet.

Chapter Twenty-four

THE LAST NAIL

T he entry of America and her allies into the Asian war, as a result of the Japanese attack on Pearl Harbour, raised the hopes of the long-suffering Chinese people, to whom it had begun to appear that there might never be another dawn for their harassed country. Chungking shared this optimism, but it tinged it with a faint cynicism which reflected the decadence that was sapping the strength of the capital. Giovanni comments on the news briefly:

'There is a great deal of hope aroused by the entry of the U.S.A. into the war. Government people think that now there will be an end to all this shilly-shallying and that we shall get real aid at last in our fight. However, there are doubts whether America can do anything really effective in actual military operations. Our Chinese soldiers, with their long and bitter experience of fighting, are inclined, even in this wave of hope and excitement, to take the view that they are amateur theorists more likely to cause trouble. For myself I feel that unrestricted supplies would be the best and most valuable aid that America could give us. . . .'

In due course, an American invasion of Chungking took place—missions, observers, and the rest, whose purpose was to establish close relations. There was keen and constant competition for the favours of these newcomers, as Giovanni observes:

'A new scramble is going on in the city for the dollars and influence of our new American visitors and allies.

The Last Nail

Money changers are making huge profits on the official rate of exchange between Chinese and American dollars, and the Americans love of souvenirs is proving a gold mine to the shopkeepers and street vendors. I don't think the Americans have yet woken up to the fact that perhaps a half of the "Chinese works of art" they are buying are fakes produced in Japan and smuggled over from the Japanese-occupied areas. This is all part of the present state of affairs in China, and I do not see how it can be remedied. . . .'

That depressing and enervating attitude of *laisser-faire* which had come over Giovanni reveals itself again even in a comment like this. He sees an evil and even, by implication, condemns it; but he does not see what can be done about it. It is there; it is established; it is better left untouched lest worse befall. That seems to sum up the new philosophy of Giovanni, the man who would once have been prepared to face by himself the whole world in arms, when his indignation and sympathy had been aroused. He did not even seem to have any idea of honesty or fairness left, for he can openly record in his diary:

'Passing along the street today I was called upon for aid by an American who had got into an argument with a shopkeeper. It was over a vase, which the shopkeeper alleged was genuine Ming, though a glance was sufficient to show that it was one of the least convincing of fakes. The American implored me to argue with the man and knock down his price; he was not questioning the authenticity of the piece but thought the price too high. All I could do was to say that if it was a genuine Ming then what the shopkeeper was asking was a long way below its real value, but I was no expert on pottery. There I left them, though glancing back I believe I saw that the American had clinched the bargain. What does it matter? The American will no doubt gloat over his purchase and show it to his friends, no less ignorant than himself, and a Chinese trader will have got some useful

American dollars. The Americans can spare them, and the Chinese are very poor. . . .'

He was now clearly identifying himself with the Chinese themselves, though in a rather patronizing sort of way.

Apart from the arrival of the Americans in the city, the new phase of the war made little difference to life in Chungking. So many Americans with ideas and authority meant, of course, that the pace of intrigue and backdoor dealing quickened perceptibly. It was necessary now to ingratiate oneself not only with the lords of the Kuomintang but also with the new allies who, from the first, had demonstrated quite clearly that they were ready to be the paymaster of the Kuomintang and support it at all costs. For a little while American supremacy was high; it was better to have the friendship of an American than of a Chinese, no matter how high his position. The series of disasters to British, Dutch, and Americans, in the early stages of the Pacific war, disasters that seemed to show the invincibility of Japan, altered all this considerably, and the first hopes gave way to despondency. Giovanni writes of this period:

'The prestige of the European was never lower in China than it is today. Quite ordinary people here are asking how it is that China, with no arms and resources, has been able to hold Japan at bay for so long, while countries like England and America, great powers with every advantage, are unable even to defend their important bases in the Pacific. At times the Americans have to face open ridicule in the streets. I am glad that I have been here long enough to have established myself as part of the Chinese machine; otherwise I might find my life rather unpleasant. . . . '

He attended a reception at one of the American headquarters in the city and there he saw Garrow, the first contact he had made with the American since the memorable interview that had set his foot firmly on the ladder of position. He observes—and it is a revealing statement of his changed mentality:

'Almost the first person I saw in the room was Garrow. Recalling the snub he had given me, I was not inclined to be friendly, and when he had the effrontery to give me a nod and smile of recognition across the length of the room, I returned his salutations very coldly, and turned to speak to my neighbour. But he worked his way through the mob to me and insisted on talking to me. He said he wondered how I had been getting on. I replied that I was well satisfied with my lot, but that the Americans didn't seem to be getting on so very well, and that perhaps after all China had a little to teach them. That made him dry up somewhat, for after a few more desultory remarks, he shrugged his shoulders and moved away.

'Far more exciting was another encounter with a late arrival. This was none other than my old friend Butts, the young English doctor who had worked with me in those incredible guerilla days. He looked tired and worn, but very tough and hard, and was wearing a very shabby uniform of the Eighth Route Army. I was glad to see him, but he seems to have changed a great deal for he was very reserved with me and I did not like some of his remarks.

'I asked him what he was doing now. He replied that he was on the same old job, though conditions were a bit better now. The guerillas were still active in the north-east and he was working with them. Immediately I said I could do something to get him out of it as I had influence. He gave me one of those insolent half smiles which are so characteristically English and told me he was quite happy where he was doing a real job, and he said it in a way that was not far from insulting. Still, that kind of service produces odd streaks in a man, and I was prepared to overlook it. Then I asked him what he was doing in Chungking, and this time there could be no condoning his rudeness. He replied—these are his very words: "I'm here to do the very thing you came to Chungking to do— find out why we don't get our full quota of medical

supplies, and I'm going to tear Hell wide open until I do
get them." And he added nastily: "If I go to the S.N.D.C.
it won't be as a hanger-on but with a gun to shoot some
sense and honesty into them." I said something polite
and walked away. I do not think he was trying to be
deliberately insulting; it is merely that he envies me my
success, and like so many unambitious people seeks to
belittle it. . . .'

When Butts Colson called at Giovanni's office a week
later, Giovanni thought it was to offer apologies, but far
from it:

'An unexpected visitor at the office—Butts. I thought
he had probably come to apologize for his conduct the
other night, which reflection must surely have shown him
to be in the worst possible taste. I greeted him as though
nothing had happened and gave him every chance of making
an *amende honorable*, but he said nothing. Instead he asked
for a favour—which was surely adding insult to injury.
He said I had offered to help him to a job. He didn't
want a job but he wanted to know if I could break down
some of the walls that separated him from seeing the
people he wanted to see. "I hate doing this," he said.
"When human lives are at stake, there shouldn't be any
of this sort of thing. But this place stinks of corruption,
and I suppose I've got to play the game according to the
rules. We belong to different worlds now, Giovanni, but
I ask you out of old comradeship and in memory of your
once being a good doctor." He could hardly have put a
request for a favour more offensively, especially as he
added: "I am sorry I can't offer anything in exchange.
I've been too busy fighting to have anything at all in the
world." I am always glad to help old friends, but this was
too much. He was treating me as though in some way I
was unprincipled, and I should hardly be in my present
position if I were that kind of man. So I told him,
which was quite true, that I had nothing to do with
supply matters. To gloss it over, I gave him the name
of a certain official in the proper department who

might help him. There I left it. I had done as much as anyone could have expected in return for rudeness—more in fact than he deserved. He should know that old comradeship, as he calls it, is not an excuse for everything.'

For all his superiority, Giovanni yet was sufficiently interested in his old friend to have his actions watched and reported upon—like everyone else in Chungking, Giovanni must have had his spies and informers. He found out that Butts, the despised Communist guerilla surgeon, was a better man than he expected. For Butts had in a sense followed Giovanni's example, though with very different ends. He had gone straight to the American supply mission and raised hell. As might have been expected, the Americans took a liking to this hard-hitting Englishman who knew what he wanted and intended to get it. Giovanni writes:

'Butts has no sense of decorum, and I regard his conduct in making trouble at the American mission as uncalled for and reprehensible. But the Americans have accepted his story and they have been giving the S.N.D.C. commissariat and supply sections a very bad time, threatening this, that, and the other. This sort of thing does not make a difficult life any easier. We have too much to think about in Chungking to worry about every little medical unit in the north-east that has run short of field dressings, and now we have these Americans who are trying to force things along at a quite ridiculous pace and without any regard to the rules that govern Chinese life. I am very sorry that a former colleague of mine is concerned in this affair. . . .'

There is no further mention of Butts Colson at that time. Presumably he got what he wanted. That glimpse of him is sufficient to arouse one's fullest admiration for the man, a breath of good clean air from the north that cleared away for a little the fogs of corruption and unreality that hung even more thickly than the physical fogs over Chungking.

It is here that Giovanni's diary becomes rather tenuous. He no longer records all his reactions to the petty affairs of life, and such comments as he does make are without much value, except as revealing a man whose mind had become sunk in sloth and mistook every piece of tinsel for a golden crown. The Generalissimo fell ill, and every doctor in the place was summoned. Giovanni, of course, was among the first half-dozen, and he notes the fact with relish:

'It was deeply gratifying to think that I have been one of the first doctors to be called in to the Generalissimo in his regrettable illness. Luckily I find myself in agreement with my colleagues that there is nothing seriously wrong. The Generalissimo has been straining his wonderful vitality beyond even its capacity for endurance, and the result is that he needs rest, careful dieting, and a course of building up. Among the doctors present was the principal military surgeon of the American mission. I spoke to him for quite a few minutes, and he seemed very impressed by the way in which we are organizing the medical services of the Chinese Army. . . .'

So far as the diary material goes, the inference is that Giovanni had less and less to do. More and more of the practical direction of the war was being taken over by the Americans (who, in the end, had virtually to assume direction of the entire Chinese war effort) and the heavily overweighted Chungking organizations became bogged under their own weight. Probably Giovanni's existence had been largely forgotten. He was there on the payroll, and nothing had occurred to force his removal. Therefore he stayed; and with American money to back it lavishly, the Central Government was not over-inclined to economize in looking after its friends.

Meanwhile the war went on. Japan dominated the Pacific. The guerillas fought heroically in China. The sky looked black. And then in 1944 the tide turned. Already the defeat of Japan took shape and the Chinese people heaved a sigh of relief. Giovanni had weathered every change of fortune, every turn of history. He was 'a subordinate member of the S.N.D.C.', still drawing his salary for practically no work, still enjoying with Lydia such delights as Chungking had to offer—and now they were somewhat richer, since the Americans had brought wealth and supplies to the city and insisted, in their way, on the provision of ample relaxation for their people, in which the other citizens shared.

It was during 1945 that Giovanni made the following comment, one of the very few in that year that are anything else but repetitions of a profound and uncritical acceptance of life as it is and of undiluted egotism:

'This has become an American city. Everything has been Americanized, for the American believes that his own way of life is the ideal for all peoples. But in some ways this process has yielded an improvement. The town is gayer and brighter. Even the Generalissimo has relaxed some of the strict rules he has hitherto enjoined on his subjects. Thus, Chinese may now attend dances even when Europeans are not present. Chinese girls no longer have to have their hair permanently waved surreptitiously: they can go openly to the hairdresser without fear of adverse comment or reproof. And there is more and better food about, especially for Europeans. One can now dine reasonably, with good food and even good wine occasionally. It is expensive, but it enables one to forget the horrors of war. . . .'

'The horrors of war!' The phrase comes oddly from a man living the life that Giovanni had since he had settled in Chungking. Yet perhaps he was right; perhaps, in the last summing up, it will be seen that Chungking itself was one of the most malodorous horrors of war, unrelieved by any of that quiet bravery and devotion, that fortitude and comradeship, which give to the real horrors of the battlefield an aura of eternal glory.

When the end was in sight, the Russians declared war on Japan and began a drive eastwards against a crumbling opposition. Giovanni was wrapped up in his own trivial affairs. He wrote:

'The Russians have come in force now to Chungking. It is another foreign invasion. I suppose that when the Japs are ended we shall find that we are controlled by the Americans and the Russians and that the Chinese themselves and those who have given their lives to the cause of China have no say in the matter at all. There is no love lost between the Russians and the Americans, though openly they are very friendly. America has placed herself squarely and, as I think, wisely behind Chiang Kai-shek, while the Russians, naturally, are supporters of the Communists, who now control a large part of the north, which does not augur well for the future of the country. These are matters that do not really concern me. When the war is over, Lydia and I will have to examine the situation and decide what is our best course for a new life. Luckily the war has not brought me only bad luck. I have managed to build up quite a useful reserve of American dollars which will go far to making me independent. There may be a chance that I can return to Italy, now that Fascism is dead there, though not if it turns Communist. I have come to regard Communism as the epitome of all evil. It forces poor people of no particular abilities, who are quite happy in their simple tasks, to take exaggerated ideas of their own importance and become hostile to those who, like our own Generalissimo, have the welfare and prosperity of the whole country and not just one section of it at heart. . . .'

That was, to my mind, the last nail in the coffin of the Giovanni I had known and admired. He had forsaken everything that had once been sacred to him. The philosophy of the Kuomintang, with its emphasis on wealth and privilege, had sunk into his bones, and he had lost all sympathy and contact with the common people from whom he himself had sprung and in whom he once had a passionate belief. He had forgotten even that he was a doctor—the last and most incredible change of all.

The Last Nail

It was not quite the end. A man does not turn from burning idealism to place hunting, from disinterested service to self-seeking, without laying up trouble for himself. Nemesis sometimes strikes in the right place, for all her alleged blindness; and when the first Russian mission arrived in Chungking, she was already beginning to play her hand in her game against Giovanni.

Chapter Twenty-five

ARREST

VJ-Day brought little more than an illusion of peace to China. The defeat of Japan after the atomic bombing of Hiroshima and Nagasaki gave the people for a short while an impression that now, at last, they could settle down to rebuilding their ravaged and exhausted country. The basic sorrows of China remained. There were still floods, famines, diseases, all of which war had made worse. The Japs had wrecked much of the little that pre-war China had been able to do to check these menaces. But for a little while China had known the joys of a united spirit and a common endeavour, and the people hoped, as the rest of the world did, that those qualities would carry them through the problems of peace.

But China's problems had only been shelved; they had not been solved or even put into proper perspective. In the heart of the Kuomintang was the ingrained belief that they alone had the right to rule and mould China. From that sprang their undying hostility to Communism, which was now strong as never before. What had happened before in China was re-enacted. She turned from one war to another, from war with a foreigner to war within herself.

It is necessary briefly to recall these facts to set the stage for the last act of Giovanni's tragedy. Beside the great tragedy of China itself, his is a small and trivial one, it is true, yet it is the theme of this book and will be followed to the end.

He offers an illuminating observation or two on the position at the end of the war:

'Everyone is glad that hostilities are over and that China is freed at last of the menace of the Japs. For Lydia and myself it opens up new possibilities of rest and relief from many straining years. Yet talking to the Kuomintang people, as I often do, and taken into their confidence, it is a pity in many ways that the peace could not have been postponed. The Communists control much of the north-east and north-west, including, unhappily, a large stretch of the important coast area. The National Armies are a consider-able distance away, and at best it must be some time before they can reach these territories. So again we are faced with a divided China, for it is obvious that the Communists, who claim that they have played the major part in ensuring victory, are not going to accept without question control by the Generalissimo and his advisers. This is a dangerous situation, especially as the Russians are doing so much to encourage the Chinese Communists in their intransigence. . . .'

This was a good summing up from the official point of view, which Giovanni now so meekly accepted because he was part of the official machine. In those few lines is given the reason for Chiang's almost immediately embarking upon another war. Just as overnight he had come to an agreement with the Communists at Sian, so now he threw that agreement away. No doubt he had provocation, but few will assert that it is good statesmanship to fly to the sword except as a last resort—especially to thrust it into the body of one's own people. A new civil war broke out, a civil war that is still being fought and of which the end cannot be foreseen, any more than the cold war in the rest of the world has any predictable finish. The post-war years have brought renewed misery to China, and their political history is one of gigantic blunders on both sides. The Americans have sent every possible aid to Chiang. The Russians have stood firmly behind the Communists. In China the germs of trouble still seethe and multiply.

In Chungking, the foreign mission and embassies re-mained. There were British and French, Americans and

Russians. But it was the two last-named that dominated the scene. Giovanni comments acidly on this:

'I cannot take to the Russians,' he says. 'I cannot see that they did anything to defeat Japan; they merely walked in to assist in carving up the carcase, and that seems to me absolutely no justification for their conduct here. They are overbearing and aggressive, insolent and bad-mannered. Chungking, in fact, has become a battle-ground in which the Americans and the Russians are fighting out their claims to dominate China. It is for this, then, that some of us have devoted all energies during these trying years of war. . . .'

He still retained his post, and curiously now that the war was over he found himself with more work to do. Increasingly he was called in to treat eminent members of the Government proper and the Kuomintang—and not simply to give a formal second opinion but to take charge of the cases. This pleased him:

'At least the Chinese are not without gratitude,' he remarks. 'It would have been easy for them to have dismissed their foreign helpers. With me at any rate it is otherwise. I find myself in a stronger position than ever before. Some of the other foreign doctors have gone back to their own countries and that leaves me as practically the senior honorary physician to the members of the Government. I find my services in increasing demand. That is gratifying enough, but what is even more pleasurable is that the highest-placed ministers and officials repose the utmost confidence in me. Often they discuss with me confidential matters of the highest importance which, of course, I cannot repeat even in the secret pages of my diary. I am right at the heart of things now, secure, respected, and trusted. For this reason alone I cannot consider leaving China. . . .'

Yet there were difficulties, and they arose through Lydia.

'Lydia is very strange nowadays,' he confided to his diary. 'She is restless and distraught and obviously needs a change and rest. It is impossible for me to ask for leave at the present time, as I have one or two important cases on hand, and a certain minister has begged me to remain with him while he handles a very delicate matter—he feels that the strain of it may cause him to fall ill and he would like me to be at hand, which is very flattering, and a request I cannot refuse. So I have suggested to Lydia that she might take a holiday on her own. She could go to America and really enjoy life for a few months. There are ample dollars there for her to spend, and I know she would have a good time. To my surprise she refuses point blank—not only that but every suggestion that she should go to one of the better resorts in China itself. She does not want to leave Chungking, she says. I am not sure that that is not a dangerous sign, indicating some sort of obsession of which she should be cured. . . .'

It was indeed a dangerous sign but not in the way he imagined, as events were to show. But in the meantime there is a growing note of puzzlement in the entries:

'I called on one of my patients today—a man high up in the personal counsel of the Generalissimo himself; I mention no names for obvious reasons—and I found him unusually cold and reserved. I mentioned a matter we had discussed quite freely at my previous visit, but he refused to discuss it, saying that it was now in such a delicate stage that he could barely trust himself with what he knew. Of course I did not press the matter, but the change from complete confidence to taciturnity has been something of a shock to me. . . .'

Again, a few days later, he writes:

'In my office work, I am now almost entirely ignored. The papers put on my desk are those which, in the past, never got further than one or other of my secretaries, routine things that they could approve formally on my behalf. My advice is never sought on any matter of importance. Yesterday I put forward a suggestion on my own responsibility. The secretary of the committee said he thought it would be better not to raise the matter with

s

the department, which was much burdened with work. Yet only a week ago, a minister had requested that I should give my thoughts to the matter and send in a report as soon as I should have considered it in detail. . . .'

He went to a reception and records this of it:

'I am completely puzzled by the curious change that has come over almost everybody. No one was actually rude to me at the reception but I had the feeling that everyone I spoke to was anxious to break off the conversation at the earliest possible moment so as to avoid being seen talking to me. This, coupled with the other rebuffs I have had lately, is a strong suggestion that in some way I have offended against some of the rules, yet though I have carefully reviewed my whole actions I can find absolutely nothing to justify it. My conduct has, I think, been irreproachable. . . .'

His entries are more frequent now and they all harp on this one theme. He is being 'dropped', he says. He finds it difficult to gain entry to places at which recently he was a welcome guest. The final thrust was when the Generalissimo had a slight indisposition—and another doctor was called. It was this which decided him to take action.

'After this final evidence of my unpopularity, I decided to take the matter to the chief of the health department. I put my case plainly to him,' he writes, 'so that there could be no possible misunderstanding. I was met with polite surprise at my attitude. The minister pointed out to me that the Generalissimo shared with the humblest Chinese the right to select any doctor he chose and that I had no grounds for complaint. I replied that it had been understood I should act as the Generalissimo's chief medical adviser, but he denied all knowledge of any such arrangement, which he said was almost impossible because the Generalissimo did not bind himself in advance to any course of conduct. I felt I had made matters worse by appearing to criticize one of the Generalissimo's decisions. . . .'

The storm was now blowing up in good earnest. The next significant entry shows it almost at its height:

'Today has been one of the worst I have ever known, all the more so because I have been unable, for the first time for many years, to call upon Lydia for help and comfort. She has been out all day in the car, a form of relaxation to which she has grown much addicted and which I encourage in view of her state of health; she needs to get free of this place. The first indication of trouble was early this morning, when a messenger came with a letter for me. I was flabbergasted when I saw that it contained a summons to go to the police department—the secret police department at that. But I had a clear conscience. Perhaps I was needed as a witness. When I arrived, I was shown every courtesy and had an interview at once with the Chief himself—a man I have met many times and who, like so many of these modern Chinese, speaks mostly in English.

'He chatted for a little while and then suddenly he looked me full in the eyes and rapped a question.

' "You know why you're here, I take it?" he said.

'I said I did not. He looked puzzled, because it must have been obvious to him that I was speaking the truth. I had not the slightest idea. Then I added: "I have been waiting for you to tell me, for I am quite in the dark."

'He did not speak for a little while but sank his head in thought. At last he spoke very slowly and so softly I could barely hear him.

' "If I were you, doctor," he said, "I should make arrangements at once to leave the country. You have, I believe, money in America. I will see you have a passport. Do not delay too long. It will be good for your health to go. You need a rest."

'I was thunderstruck. I was being dismissed from the country. I was not surprised at what he knew of my private affairs as regards money; the secret police know everything. That was why I had felt so safe. I had nothing to hide.

'I pressed him for an explanation. I said I could not leave China like that. I had spent many years in China and sacrificed for her service all my connections in Europe and elsewhere, and I would be homeless. He did nothing but repeat his advice in a more insistent tone. So I left him. I wish Lydia were here to discuss it. . . .'

Lydia returned, but was unhelpful. He made another entry that same night.

'I have spoken to Lydia but all she will say is that she cannot understand it. She seems quite unwilling to talk about it. If I must go, she says, I must, but she will remain in China. She does not want to leave. This has shattered me. I can go nowhere without her.'

The next day he called upon the police again. His mind was made up. He could not leave China without Lydia, and she declined to move. Even then she was dragging him to his doom.

'I was shown at once into the Chief's office,' he writes. 'He did not seem surprised to see me, and he lost no time in coming to the point. "I suppose you have come to tell me you want your passport," he said.

' "No," I replied. "I am not going to leave China unless my wife and I decide to do so of our own free will. I demand an explanation of your conduct."

'He shook his head. "That is impossible," he said.

'I insisted. I refused to leave the room. I have never been so firm in my life, and at last he gave way.

'He said he would tell me something, but not all, as he could not yet. Then he began an amazing story. He said there had been leakages of secret information to the Communists for a long time, and investigations had, of course, been made. At first nothing could be discovered. A little while ago, a small Government force was cut to pieces. The only people who knew it was there were members of the S.N.D.C. who were above suspicion. Yet the Reds had sent a special expedition to intercept it. At last it turned out that I had been treating one of the ministers who knew and he admitted he had told me. With that clue all the other leakages were traced back to me. Therefore, if I wished to avoid arrest, I had better leave the country.

'I almost collapsed with astonishment. "But it is impossible!" I cried. "I have told no one."

'He was stern now. "It is impossible to deny facts. You were once a Communist doctor," he said.

'I said I was with the guerillas through necessity; that did not make me a Communist.

'He did not accept this. "You are close friends with one of the most notorious foreign Communists in the country," he said.

'I did not know what he meant and told him so. He smiled. "Dr. Colson," he explained. "The man they call Butts. He is a very dangerous Red. On his one visit to Chungking he called on you and you helped him."

'It was getting beyond me if they could turn Butts' unpleasant visit to me against me. But I maintained my denials. I could not admit something of which I was not guilty, and that puzzled him. At last he told me to go away. He would investigate further and send for me. In the meantime he advised me to remain in my apartment.

'This is driving me mad. It is beyond understanding. To make matters worse, I cannot talk to Lydia. She went out this morning and has not yet returned. It is already past midnight, and she has never been as late as this. I have paced my room for hours tortured by the thought of all this and wondering where she is and if anything has happened to her. That would be the blow from which I could never recover. . . .'

At dawn he wrote again in his diary in a shaky hand:

'Lydia has not returned, and I am distracted. The whole world has gone mad. If only she would come back! Every little noise outside makes me start with expectation, but always I am cast down again to the depths of despair. Lydia, my Lydia, what has happened? Now in my hour of trial I need you more than ever. . . .'

That evening he wrote again. His writing was almost

indecipherable. It was the prelude of the end, the opening chords of the coda. He wrote:

'Fate has struck remorselessly. I am still without Lydia, and now I know that I shall never see her again. It is incredible. In the light of that all else seems trivial and insignificant, but I had better set down the day's incredible events.

'I waited for Lydia. I could not eat. I had not slept all night. About nine o'clock I was called to the police. This time I was glad to see them. I asked the messenger if there was any news of Lydia; she was missing. He said he could say nothing. The Chief saw me, but he did not ask me to sit down. He kept me standing as though I was a criminal.

' "Do you still deny that you passed on secret information?" he asked sternly.

' "I have never done such a thing," I answered as firmly as I could. I was thinking of Lydia and this did not matter.

' "You are wrong, doctor," he said softly.

' "Wrong?" I repeated. He nodded.

' "You are sure you told *nobody*?" he went on. I can recall every word, every gesture.

' "Quite sure," I replied.

' "Not even your wife?" he asked.

' "Oh, yes, I mentioned one or two things to her. We had no secrets. They were as safe with her as with me," I said hotly.

' "You are wrong again," he snapped. "They were not safe with her. You told her, and she told someone else, and so much damage has been done and good Chinese lives lost." He was icy. Then he relented. "It is a blow for you, doctor. I can see that. You love your wife very much. All Chungking knows it—and sometimes they have laughed at it. They will laugh now all right. Sit down and I will tell you the whole truth." When it was over, he sent me home, telling me for the time being I was under house arrest. A guard is at the door.

Arrest

'The truth is horrible. I cannot believe it is the truth, yet I must believe. I shall have to write it down, but not now. My thoughts are a mad confusion. Yes, I shall write it down tomorrow if I am not quite mad by then. . . .'

The writing trailed away into an illegible scrawl.

Chapter Twenty-six

THE LAST TRUTH

The last pages of these diaries are wildly written. The writing is that of a man whose nerves have gone to pieces. I have done my best to decipher it. Let me set it down just as it came to me:

'Daylight has come and brought a little calm with it. All night I have paced and paced. At times I think I have been delirious, but there is no one to hear my ravings. That is the terrible part. There is *no one*. Lydia has gone, Lydia, my beloved, my world, has gone. I cannot believe it yet. I still go to the door to call out to her, listen for the sound of her feet on the stairs, the echo of her laugh. In my delirium I was back again in the north-east, tramping along the dusty roads to Yenan. That was paradise, for Lydia was there. Here is luxury, but it is hell. She has gone.

'I am still raving. I start to think and write and then the image of Lydia comes before me, and all else sinks into an indescribable background. But I must set this down. At least I know now what to do. My life is over. It existed for Lydia, and now she needs it no longer. I am glad I am a doctor. It is so easy for me. I have set my release before me—potassium cyanide acts quickly. When I have written this, that is all there is left. The more quickly I reach it the better.

'The Chief of Police told me everything. He began by being scornful and brutal, but even a policeman can be touched, and in the end he was kind and sympathetic. I am grateful to him for that. It meant a lot to me. He

280

began at the beginning, and he talked not of official secrets, but of Lydia. It cuts me, but I must write it down.

'From the moment she had won her way to Chungking and seen me established, she was unfaithful to me. Even before she had pushed me into the S.N.D.C. she had betrayed me. That job I thought so wonderful, the peak of my career, was bought for me in two ways: I was turned into a common spy, giving to the Americans information that was confidential. But also and more horribly by Lydia's kisses and Lydia's body. She gave herself to Garrow. She would, so the Chief said, have given herself to any man if the prize to be won was big enough. I wanted to cry out on him for blasphemy, but I could not. The whole terrible truth was coming on me at last and crushing me. Though I wanted to thrust it away and live on the lies I have lived on for so long. I could not. This was the last torture.

'And she had many lovers. My position in the S.N.D.C. relied upon her profligacy. While she was kind, they were kind to me. When she withdrew her favours, I was forgotten. That is a terrible and humiliating thought, yet can it be, I wonder, that she loved me so much she thought even this not too big a sacrifice to make for me?

'When the Americans came to Chungking, she was their idol. He did not tell me, nor did I ask, the details of her affairs.

'Of all this, the police took no notice. Why should they? These foreign people had strange and terrible ways. They would revile against brothels, yet they would sleep with another man's wife and feel no compunction. They tried to stamp out opium, while they soaked themselves in alcohol. So long as no harm came to the State, Lydia did not matter. I did not matter. And always she kept herself within the sacred circle of the Kuomintang. Someone had once made a joke about it. I hated the Chief of Police for repeating it, but I am trying to set down everything. It was that Lydia Campo was a part of foreign aid to China.

That went the rounds of Chungking, yet it never reached my ears.

'But it was when the Russians came that the real trouble started. She would have nothing to do with them. The authorities liked her for it, because they did not favour the Russians.

'Then the incredible happened. A certain Russian colonel was sent to Chungking, a man named, I think, if I have got it right, Limaniev, and it seems that for him Lydia conceived a real affection. It is terrible to have to write that, for I have believed that I held every particle of love of which she was capable. The others had been mere passing affairs, but this was serious. Lydia was caught in the net they spread for her. I am sure of that.

'She would do anything he asked. When she was out in the car, according to her stories, she was with him. She went to parties with him. It was a public scandal. Only I never heard of it. But the cuckold never does. He is the one man who is blind and deaf.

'Lydia was a great actress. She never let me know by a single hint that all her love was now concentrated else-where. She drew from me all my confidences, and these she betrayed to her lover, who, in turn, used them for his own ends. It was diabolical, but I have to admit that it is true.

'He did not love her. The police have their own methods of finding out the truth, and the Chief says that that is true. She was his dupe. She was as blind and trusting with him as I have been with her. I am sad for her, because I know how that feels.

'I told her of my questioning, and she saw the danger signal. She went to the colonel, begged him to take her away, protect her. And he, so the Chief says, had to accede to her wish. For, he says, he has evidence that the police were led to suspect me by an anonymous letter, which now they know to have been written by the colonel. It was a plot to get rid of me; and when I was out of the way, he could drop Lydia. But while I was still free there was danger for him. By night they left for the coast. They used an official car with escort and claimed diplomatic privilege. The Chinese could do nothing.

'That is the bare outline of the story. I do not wish to dwell upon it. I think most of all of Lydia. I do not know where she has gone, but I hope that wherever she is she will find somewhere the happiness that should be her lot.

'In this restless night I have seen many things. I have seen that I have been a fool and a coward. I have allowed myself to be duped and misled. I abandoned all the things that I used to regard—and perhaps still do in my soul— as above price: service, humanity, truth, sympathy. These I threw away to please a woman. Now she has brought me to the edge of ruin and the certainty of death.

'I blush when I remember that I have sent the record of these things for other eyes to read, for I know that the eyes that read them never looked with favour on Lydia; and now I know that view to be right.

'For I have convinced myself that she never loved me. She came to me only when all else had failed her, when Italy and even Europe were unsafe for her. She thought she saw a way out by way of the Communist guerillas, and she forced me to it. She had courage and endurance, for she stood up to much that would have killed a strong man, let alone a woman. But she was animated not by any sense of service or love for me, but only by her own ambition. She wanted to be great, to enjoy luxury, and she was willing to pay any price for it. So, in the end, she brought me to Chungking, where I have become a spiritual prostitute, the handmaiden of Chinese corruption, a cuckold, and a laughing-stock. For when I thought I was eminent, I was a joke.

'Those things are clear to me now. I see them all. I see Lydia for the sort of woman she is, self-centred, ambitious, using all men and all things for her own ends, and those ends were in themselves petty and despicable. I have earned doubly the right to die. It is the one right left to me to exercise, and I shall do so.

The Last Truth

'But let me not go out of this world into whatever lies beyond without making these, my last words, a vehicle of the whole truth. I am disgraced. I have failed in all I set out to do—even in the end of making Lydia happy. I have become the least of men. Yet let it not be thought that I am bitter or resentful. Above all let no one think that overnight I have grown to hate Lydia. That could never be.

'I have paced my room and reviewed my whole life. I have lived again those happy days when I fought against the Fascists and the days in the mission field. I have fought again with the guerillas. I have played at being great in Chungking. I have experienced all the agonies of manifold betrayal. Yet if I had my life again I would not wish it to be other than it is. For the greatest experience of my life has been and remains loving Lydia.

'She is black, evil, and faithless; but I love her above all else. She did not love me; any other man might have served her purpose, and she would have taken him and betrayed him. But I am grateful that she chose me. We lived together through times that searched our very souls. In hers was found ambition; in mine love for her. And when the last judgment is made it will still be found there.

'Happiness is a strange thing, love is a strange thing. The two are not the same, as so many think. There is happiness in love, but in the deepest love there is more of suffering. Loving is giving, not taking. To Lydia I gave everything; and there is nothing I would take back even if I had the chance.

'But with her going, there is an end of me. I cannot go out to face life anew, because life now has no meaning for me. This is a wound that an eternity of time could not heal. She has gone and with her she has taken all of me that meant anything. She had moulded it to her own shape and it is hers.

'And now it is goodbye. I have made my confession. In a little while this which the world knew as Giovanni

Campo will be no more than a collection of proteins falling into disorganization. But I shall live as long as Lydia does; I am a part of her. To her I cannot say goodbye. But to those others who have been kind to me, I say farewell. To you, George, for whom these lines are written, for as firm and true a friendship as ever man enjoyed, a friendship that was undeserved, for so often I denied its obligations and refused to listen to the wise advice that sprang from it. To Butts, my colleague in the guerillas, as true a man as ever trod the earth, a man in whom I see myself as I should have been, giving his everything, not for the flash of a woman's smile, but for a cause that means everything to him and can enrich the world. These two I salute and bid them farewell. May God bless them. I ask that they shall not pity me. I can look steadily into the eyes of death and say that though their experiences may have been deep and enriching, they have known nothing so profound as that which, though it dragged me down in the eyes of the world, yet raised me to the highest peaks of paradise. . . .'

That was all, but for one thing—a scrawled note saying that he had arranged for these papers to be sent to me. It was the end of Giovanni Campo.

EPILOGUE

I did not know the name of the man who had asked to see me, saying he was not a patient. But curiosity being my strongest vice, I told the receptionist to show him in. He was tall, muscular, wiry, with no spare flesh anywhere. His face and manner had the hallmarks of one who has seen suffering and hardship at its worst. His skin had the curious colour of one who has lived in the least attractive climates of the world. And he eyed me steadily and with a faint twinkle.

'You did not give your name?' I said vaguely, as though I had foolishly forgotten it.

'No,' he said. 'It's Colson—my nickname is Butts. You have read about me, I think.'

Beyond a certain familiarity, I could not place it; then it dawned upon me. This was Butts of Giovanni's diaries! I wrung his hand warmly and settled him in my best chair.

'You got the last packet of diaries?' he asked.

'Yes. You sent them?'

He nodded. 'Yes. Giovanni was a queer bloke—remarkably cool in some things. He managed to send out that last packet by one of his servants and he got it through to me via the Communists. He thought it all out as the safest way. A note asked me to send it on. When the servant came back and reported that he had handed it over, he locked the door, telephoned the police, and then killed himself. A really massive dose of potassium cyanide—he must have been dead in seconds.'

He told me more. He was on leave in England after many years, and he had resolved to see me if he could. And he talked of Giovanni.

Epilogue

'That woman was his blind spot, but it was no good telling him of it,' he said. 'He was the one sighted man in the world where that was concerned. What a career he could have had but for her!'

I nodded. 'Yes. You never heard anything of Lydia?'

'No,' he replied. 'Why should I? I hope she has gone to the Devil by the least comfortable route.'

He left me later, promising to call again, but he never came. And that was the last news I ever had of Giovanni Campo.

I have told his tale, as far as possible in his own words, in these pages. Perhaps it is a commonplace tale—the tale of a man who gave all for a woman and in the end was betrayed—a tale that is being repeated over and over again all over the world at this very minute, and will go on being repeated so long as there are men to love and women ready to make use of love but not return it. Yet it has something which should be recorded permanently. It brings into focus that everlasting problem of the white man and the East. Against more accustomed backgrounds would Giovanni have behaved as he did? Would he not have been constrained in a different climate of culture, in less exotic circumstances?

Sometimes I think he would. But in the end I decide that he would not. For Giovanni had in him all the mysterious power of genius. He could have been a world-renowned physician, a man to whom grateful men and women looked with respect and devotion. He could also have been a powerful and enlightened missionary. He could have been a leader of men in freedom, swaying them and inspiring them to exploits and achievements beyond their capacity. But he chose, instead, to divert all that genius he possessed into the channel of a great and overmastering love. And who shall say that, though it brought him tragedy, he was wrong? Is not love, show itself how it will, the greatest of all human emotions, from which all others spring?